10,000 HOURS

A JOURNAL FOR YOUR 10,000 HOUR JOURNEY FROM ABSOLUTE BEGINNER TO EXPERT

D1214829

THE PRODUCTIVE LUDDITE™

PAPER. PRODUCTIVITY. CREATIVITY. BETTER LIVING.

VITAL INFORMATION

THIS JOURNAL IS OWNED & OPERATED BY

DID YOU FIND MY JOURNAL?
PLEASE RETURN TO / PLEASE CONTACT

REWARD: ○ THE WARM FEELING OF DOING GOOD
○ COLD HARD CASH $_____
○ ALL OF THE ABOVE

START DATE   **END DATE**

SUBJECT MATTER   **VOLUME / ID#**

SUMMARY / ABSTRACT

ABOUT THE JOURNEY

© 2010 Productive Luddite
All Rights Reserved.
Printed in the United States, ironically, by machines.
Designed in Canada.
ISBN: 978-1-926892-36-8

Do you have any suggestions for improving this product or any of The Productive Luddite's products? Please send email to: info@productiveluddite.com.

www.ProductiveLuddite.com

HOW TO USE THIS JOURNAL

GENIUS IS A SPECIES OF EXPERTISE

No one is born a genius; genius is a species of expertise; and expertise is always a by-product of mixing the following ingredients: luck, opportunity, coaching, mentoring, and sustained, premeditated practice or study. Next to sustained, pre-planned practice or study, talent is almost irrelevant. When you see this list of ingredients, you should be excited. By committing to and starting your 10,000 hour journey, it is entirely possible that all of these ingredients will fall into place for you. Here's why:

1. The harder you work, the luckier you get.
2. The more you learn, the smarter you work.
3. The smarter you work, the more opportunity seeks you out.
4. The more you seek out and find great coaches and mentors, the faster you learn.
5. The degree to which you become your own best coach and mentor is the degree to which you will progress.

The 10,000 hour journey is where you discover and mix these ingredients. And, the one ingredient which you exercise the greatest degree of control over is the journey itself.

THE INTENTIONAL JOURNEY, THE INTENTIONAL JOURNAL

There are no happy accidents that turn people into experts. It doesn't happen by wishing. There are no pills or elective surgeries that will make you an expert. The journey does not take itself. You take the journey. And the only way to take the journey is by consciously planning it; by planning and taking a journey of learning, studying and practicing.

10,000 HOURS is a journal designed to help you with this intentional journey. It is a tool to help you stay focused and motivated; it helps you organize your ideas and actions as you progress along your path; and, it helps you remember the highs, the lows, and all your efforts along the way. Use this journal to record anything relevant to you and your journey of 10,000 hours. Record what you are:

*   reading,
*   researching,
*   practicing,
*   listening to,
*   feeling,
*   thinking,
*   studying,
*   the sacrifices you are making,
*   the compromises you have made or refused to make,
*   what you are learning and where you are learning it,

- who are you learning from,
- what's inspiring you,
- your motivations, motivators and demotivators,
- your current struggles and the struggles you have overcome,
- the people you meet along the way,
- the wisdom you uncover,
- the secrets you discover,
- the life lessons you learn,
- what you have mastered so far,
- what your next goal is,
- what your current stretch-goal is,
- the tools you are using or planning to use, and
- the techniques you are learning, developing, and perfecting.

Add dates and times and locations to your journal entries. Add whatever matters to you. Use this journal to take satisfaction in the work you've done and to get excited about the new things you're going to learn, do, and share.

MILESTONES
Record the milestones of your journey in the IMPORTANT MILESTONES registry at the front of your journal.

TAG YOUR JOURNEY
Towards the end of the journal, you'll find blank TAG INDEX pages. Use them to create pointers to the remarkable happenings in your journey and life. Your Tag Index makes your journey highlights or themes easy to find. You decide what's *tag-worthy*. Tags are label, category, or keyword names that help you organize your information for easy identification and retrieval.

HOW TO USE TAGS
When writing your journal entries, add in as many tags as you deem necessary. You can write tags in the margins; add them to the end of entries; use a highlighter to make them easy to see; or, reserve a special color ink for tags.

1. Every time you use a tag in your journal, flip to the Tag Index at the back.
2. If the tag does not yet exist in the Tag Index, enter it in the index and record the hour or page number next to it.
3. If the tag does exist, locate it, and enter the relevant hour or page number.

RECOMMENDED READING
- K. Anders Ericsson, Michael J. Prietula, and Edward T. Cokely. "Making of an Expert." *Harvard Business Review*. July-August 2007. pp 115-121.
- Malcolm Gladwell. *Outliers: The Story of Success*. Little, Brown and Company. 2008.
- Geoff Colvin. *Talent Is Overrated: What Really Separates World-Class Performers from Everybody Else*. Portfolio Hardcover. 2008.

IMPORTANT MILESTONES

HOUR	MILESTONE

HOUR	MILESTONE

Hour	COUNTDOWN
1	10,000
2	9,999
3	9,998
4	9,997
5	9,996
6	9,995
7	9,994
8	9,993
9	9,992
10	9,991
11	9,990
12	9,989
13	9,988
14	9,987
15	9,986
16	9,985
17	9,984

Hour	COUNTDOWN
18	9,983
19	9,982
20	9,981
21	9,980
22	9,979
23	9,978
24	9,977
25	9,976
26	9,975
27	9,974
28	9,973
29	9,972
30	9,971
31	9,970
32	9,969
33	9,968
34	9,967

Hour	COUNTDOWN
35	9,966
36	9,965
37	9,964
38	9,963
39	9,962
40	9,961
41	9,960
42	9,959
43	9,958
44	9,957
45	9,956
46	9,955
47	9,954
48	9,953
49	9,952
50	9,951
51	9,950

Hour	COUNTDOWN
52	9,949
53	9,948
54	9,947
55	9,946
56	9,945
57	9,944
58	9,943
59	9,942
60	9,941
61	9,940
62	9,939
63	9,938
64	9,937
65	9,936
66	9,935
67	9,934
68	9,933

Hour	COUNTDOWN
69	9,932
70	9,931
71	9,930
72	9,929
73	9,928
74	9,927
75	9,926
76	9,925
77	9,924
78	9,923
79	9,922
80	9,921
81	9,920
82	9,919
83	9,918
84	9,917
85	9,916

Hour	COUNTDOWN
86	9,915
87	9,914
88	9,913
89	9,912
90	9,911
91	9,910
92	9,909
93	9,908
94	9,907
95	9,906
96	9,905
97	9,904
98	9,903
99	9,902
100	9,901
101	9,900
102	9,899

Hour	COUNTDOWN
103	9,898
104	9,897
105	9,896
106	9,895
107	9,894
108	9,893
109	9,892
110	9,891
111	9,890
112	9,889
113	9,888
114	9,887
115	9,886
116	9,885
117	9,884
118	9,883
119	9,882

Hour	COUNTDOWN
120	9,881
121	9,880
122	9,879
123	9,878
124	9,877
125	9,876
126	9,875
127	9,874
128	9,873
129	9,872
130	9,871
131	9,870
132	9,869
133	9,868
134	9,867
135	9,866
136	9,865

Hour	COUNTDOWN
137	9,864
138	9,863
139	9,862
140	9,861
141	9,860
142	9,859
143	9,858
144	9,857
145	9,856
146	9,855
147	9,854
148	9,853
149	9,852
150	9,851
151	9,850
152	9,849
153	9,848

Hour	COUNTDOWN
154	9,847
155	9,846
156	9,845
157	9,844
158	9,843
159	9,842
160	9,841
161	9,840
162	9,839
163	9,838
164	9,837
165	9,836
166	9,835
167	9,834
168	9,833
169	9,832
170	9,831

Hour	COUNTDOWN
171	9,830
172	9,829
173	9,828
174	9,827
175	9,826
176	9,825
177	9,824
178	9,823
179	9,822
180	9,821
181	9,820
182	9,819
183	9,818
184	9,817
185	9,816
186	9,815
187	9,814

Hour	COUNTDOWN
188	9,813
189	9,812
190	9,811
191	9,810
192	9,809
193	9,808
194	9,807
195	9,806
196	9,805
197	9,804
198	9,803
199	9,802
200	9,801
201	9,800
202	9,799
203	9,798
204	9,797

Hour	COUNTDOWN
205	9,796
206	9,795
207	9,794
208	9,793
209	9,792
210	9,791
211	9,790
212	9,789
213	9,788
214	9,787
215	9,786
216	9,785
217	9,784
218	9,783
219	9,782
220	9,781
221	9,780

Hour	COUNTDOWN
222	9,779
223	9,778
224	9,777
225	9,776
226	9,775
227	9,774
228	9,773
229	9,772
230	9,771
231	9,770
232	9,769
233	9,768
234	9,767
235	9,766
236	9,765
237	9,764
238	9,763

Hour	COUNTDOWN
239	9,762
240	9,761
241	9,760
242	9,759
243	9,758
244	9,757
245	9,756
246	9,755
247	9,754
248	9,753
249	9,752
250	9,751
251	9,750
252	9,749
253	9,748
254	9,747
255	9,746

Hour	COUNTDOWN
256	9,745
257	9,744
258	9,743
259	9,742
260	9,741
261	9,740
262	9,739
263	9,738
264	9,737
265	9,736
266	9,735
267	9,734
268	9,733
269	9,732
270	9,731
271	9,730
272	9,729

Hour	COUNTDOWN
273	9,728
274	9,727
275	9,726
276	9,725
277	9,724
278	9,723
279	9,722
280	9,721
281	9,720
282	9,719
283	9,718
284	9,717
285	9,716
286	9,715
287	9,714
288	9,713
289	9,712

Hour	COUNTDOWN
290	9,711
291	9,710
292	9,709
293	9,708
294	9,707
295	9,706
296	9,705
297	9,704
298	9,703
299	9,702
300	9,701
301	9,700
302	9,699
303	9,698
304	9,697
305	9,696
306	9,695

Hour	COUNTDOWN
307	9,694
308	9,693
309	9,692
310	9,691
311	9,690
312	9,689
313	9,688
314	9,687
315	9,686
316	9,685
317	9,684
318	9,683
319	9,682
320	9,681
321	9,680
322	9,679
323	9,678

Hour	COUNTDOWN
324	9,677
325	9,676
326	9,675
327	9,674
328	9,673
329	9,672
330	9,671
331	9,670
332	9,669
333	9,668
334	9,667
335	9,666
336	9,665
337	9,664
338	9,663
339	9,662
340	9,661

Hour	COUNTDOWN
341	9,660
342	9,659
343	9,658
344	9,657
345	9,656
346	9,655
347	9,654
348	9,653
349	9,652
350	9,651
351	9,650
352	9,649
353	9,648
354	9,647
355	9,646
356	9,645
357	9,644

Hour	COUNTDOWN
358	9,643
359	9,642
360	9,641
361	9,640
362	9,639
363	9,638
364	9,637
365	9,636
366	9,635
367	9,634
368	9,633
369	9,632
370	9,631
371	9,630
372	9,629
373	9,628
374	9,627

Hour	COUNTDOWN
375	9,626
376	9,625
377	9,624
378	9,623
379	9,622
380	9,621
381	9,620
382	9,619
383	9,618
384	9,617
385	9,616
386	9,615
387	9,614
388	9,613
389	9,612
390	9,611
391	9,610

Hour	COUNTDOWN
392	9,609
393	9,608
394	9,607
395	9,606
396	9,605
397	9,604
398	9,603
399	9,602
400	9,601
401	9,600
402	9,599
403	9,598
404	9,597
405	9,596
406	9,595
407	9,594
408	9,593

Hour	COUNTDOWN
409	9,592
410	9,591
411	9,590
412	9,589
413	9,588
414	9,587
415	9,586
416	9,585
417	9,584
418	9,583
419	9,582
420	9,581
421	9,580
422	9,579
423	9,578
424	9,577
425	9,576

Hour	COUNTDOWN
426	9,575
427	9,574
428	9,573
429	9,572
430	9,571
431	9,570
432	9,569
433	9,568
434	9,567
435	9,566
436	9,565
437	9,564
438	9,563
439	9,562
440	9,561
441	9,560
442	9,559

Hour	COUNTDOWN
443	9,558
444	9,557
445	9,556
446	9,555
447	9,554
448	9,553
449	9,552
450	9,551
451	9,550
452	9,549
453	9,548
454	9,547
455	9,546
456	9,545
457	9,544
458	9,543
459	9,542

Hour	COUNTDOWN
460	9,541
461	9,540
462	9,539
463	9,538
464	9,537
465	9,536
466	9,535
467	9,534
468	9,533
469	9,532
470	9,531
471	9,530
472	9,529
473	9,528
474	9,527
475	9,526
476	9,525

Hour	COUNTDOWN
477	9,524
478	9,523
479	9,522
480	9,521
481	9,520
482	9,519
483	9,518
484	9,517
485	9,516
486	9,515
487	9,514
488	9,513
489	9,512
490	9,511
491	9,510
492	9,509
493	9,508

Hour	COUNTDOWN
494	9,507
495	9,506
496	9,505
497	9,504
498	9,503
499	9,502
500	9,501
501	9,500
502	9,499
503	9,498
504	9,497
505	9,496
506	9,495
507	9,494
508	9,493
509	9,492
510	9,491

Hour	COUNTDOWN
511	9,490
512	9,489
513	9,488
514	9,487
515	9,486
516	9,485
517	9,484
518	9,483
519	9,482
520	9,481
521	9,480
522	9,479
523	9,478
524	9,477
525	9,476
526	9,475
527	9,474

Hour	COUNTDOWN
528	9,473
529	9,472
530	9,471
531	9,470
532	9,469
533	9,468
534	9,467
535	9,466
536	9,465
537	9,464
538	9,463
539	9,462
540	9,461
541	9,460
542	9,459
543	9,458
544	9,457

Hour	COUNTDOWN
545	9,456
546	9,455
547	9,454
548	9,453
549	9,452
550	9,451
551	9,450
552	9,449
553	9,448
554	9,447
555	9,446
556	9,445
557	9,444
558	9,443
559	9,442
560	9,441
561	9,440

Hour	COUNTDOWN
562	9,439
563	9,438
564	9,437
565	9,436
566	9,435
567	9,434
568	9,433
569	9,432
570	9,431
571	9,430
572	9,429
573	9,428
574	9,427
575	9,426
576	9,425
577	9,424
578	9,423

Hour	COUNTDOWN
579	9,422
580	9,421
581	9,420
582	9,419
583	9,418
584	9,417
585	9,416
586	9,415
587	9,414
588	9,413
589	9,412
590	9,411
591	9,410
592	9,409
593	9,408
594	9,407
595	9,406

Hour	COUNTDOWN
596	9,405
597	9,404
598	9,403
599	9,402
600	9,401
601	9,400
602	9,399
603	9,398
604	9,397
605	9,396
606	9,395
607	9,394
608	9,393
609	9,392
610	9,391
611	9,390
612	9,389

Hour	COUNTDOWN
613	9,388
614	9,387
615	9,386
616	9,385
617	9,384
618	9,383
619	9,382
620	9,381
621	9,380
622	9,379
623	9,378
624	9,377
625	9,376
626	9,375
627	9,374
628	9,373
629	9,372

Hour	COUNTDOWN
630	9,371
631	9,370
632	9,369
633	9,368
634	9,367
635	9,366
636	9,365
637	9,364
638	9,363
639	9,362
640	9,361
641	9,360
642	9,359
643	9,358
644	9,357
645	9,356
646	9,355

Hour	COUNTDOWN
647	9,354
648	9,353
649	9,352
650	9,351
651	9,350
652	9,349
653	9,348
654	9,347
655	9,346
656	9,345
657	9,344
658	9,343
659	9,342
660	9,341
661	9,340
662	9,339
663	9,338

Hour	COUNTDOWN
664	9,337
665	9,336
666	9,335
667	9,334
668	9,333
669	9,332
670	9,331
671	9,330
672	9,329
673	9,328
674	9,327
675	9,326
676	9,325
677	9,324
678	9,323
679	9,322
680	9,321

Hour	COUNTDOWN
681	9,320
682	9,319
683	9,318
684	9,317
685	9,316
686	9,315
687	9,314
688	9,313
689	9,312
690	9,311
691	9,310
692	9,309
693	9,308
694	9,307
695	9,306
696	9,305
697	9,304

Hour	COUNTDOWN
698	9,303
699	9,302
700	9,301
701	9,300
702	9,299
703	9,298
704	9,297
705	9,296
706	9,295
707	9,294
708	9,293
709	9,292
710	9,291
711	9,290
712	9,289
713	9,288
714	9,287

Hour	COUNTDOWN
715	9,286
716	9,285
717	9,284
718	9,283
719	9,282
720	9,281
721	9,280
722	9,279
723	9,278
724	9,277
725	9,276
726	9,275
727	9,274
728	9,273
729	9,272
730	9,271
731	9,270

Hour	COUNTDOWN
732	9,269
733	9,268
734	9,267
735	9,266
736	9,265
737	9,264
738	9,263
739	9,262
740	9,261
741	9,260
742	9,259
743	9,258
744	9,257
745	9,256
746	9,255
747	9,254
748	9,253

Hour	COUNTDOWN
749	9,252
750	9,251
751	9,250
752	9,249
753	9,248
754	9,247
755	9,246
756	9,245
757	9,244
758	9,243
759	9,242
760	9,241
761	9,240
762	9,239
763	9,238
764	9,237
765	9,236

Hour	COUNTDOWN
766	9,235
767	9,234
768	9,233
769	9,232
770	9,231
771	9,230
772	9,229
773	9,228
774	9,227
775	9,226
776	9,225
777	9,224
778	9,223
779	9,222
780	9,221
781	9,220
782	9,219

Hour	COUNTDOWN
783	9,218
784	9,217
785	9,216
786	9,215
787	9,214
788	9,213
789	9,212
790	9,211
791	9,210
792	9,209
793	9,208
794	9,207
795	9,206
796	9,205
797	9,204
798	9,203
799	9,202

Hour	COUNTDOWN
800	9,201
801	9,200
802	9,199
803	9,198
804	9,197
805	9,196
806	9,195
807	9,194
808	9,193
809	9,192
810	9,191
811	9,190
812	9,189
813	9,188
814	9,187
815	9,186
816	9,185

Hour	COUNTDOWN
817	9,184
818	9,183
819	9,182
820	9,181
821	9,180
822	9,179
823	9,178
824	9,177
825	9,176
826	9,175
827	9,174
828	9,173
829	9,172
830	9,171
831	9,170
832	9,169
833	9,168

Hour	COUNTDOWN
834	9,167
835	9,166
836	9,165
837	9,164
838	9,163
839	9,162
840	9,161
841	9,160
842	9,159
843	9,158
844	9,157
845	9,156
846	9,155
847	9,154
848	9,153
849	9,152
850	9,151

Hour	COUNTDOWN
851	9,150
852	9,149
853	9,148
854	9,147
855	9,146
856	9,145
857	9,144
858	9,143
859	9,142
860	9,141
861	9,140
862	9,139
863	9,138
864	9,137
865	9,136
866	9,135
867	9,134

Hour	COUNTDOWN
868	9,133
869	9,132
870	9,131
871	9,130
872	9,129
873	9,128
874	9,127
875	9,126
876	9,125
877	9,124
878	9,123
879	9,122
880	9,121
881	9,120
882	9,119
883	9,118
884	9,117

Hour	COUNTDOWN
885	9,116
886	9,115
887	9,114
888	9,113
889	9,112
890	9,111
891	9,110
892	9,109
893	9,108
894	9,107
895	9,106
896	9,105
897	9,104
898	9,103
899	9,102
900	9,101
901	9,100

Hour	COUNTDOWN
902	9,099
903	9,098
904	9,097
905	9,096
906	9,095
907	9,094
908	9,093
909	9,092
910	9,091
911	9,090
912	9,089
913	9,088
914	9,087
915	9,086
916	9,085
917	9,084
918	9,083

Hour	COUNTDOWN
919	9,082
920	9,081
921	9,080
922	9,079
923	9,078
924	9,077
925	9,076
926	9,075
927	9,074
928	9,073
929	9,072
930	9,071
931	9,070
932	9,069
933	9,068
934	9,067
935	9,066

Hour	COUNTDOWN
936	9,065
937	9,064
938	9,063
939	9,062
940	9,061
941	9,060
942	9,059
943	9,058
944	9,057
945	9,056
946	9,055
947	9,054
948	9,053
949	9,052
950	9,051
951	9,050
952	9,049

Hour	COUNTDOWN
953	9,048
954	9,047
955	9,046
956	9,045
957	9,044
958	9,043
959	9,042
960	9,041
961	9,040
962	9,039
963	9,038
964	9,037
965	9,036
966	9,035
967	9,034
968	9,033
969	9,032

Hour	COUNTDOWN
970	9,031
971	9,030
972	9,029
973	9,028
974	9,027
975	9,026
976	9,025
977	9,024
978	9,023
979	9,022
980	9,021
981	9,020
982	9,019
983	9,018
984	9,017
985	9,016
986	9,015

Hour	COUNTDOWN
987	9,014
988	9,013
989	9,012
990	9,011
991	9,010
992	9,009
993	9,008
994	9,007
995	9,006
996	9,005
997	9,004
998	9,003
999	9,002
1,000	9,001
1,001	9,000
1,002	8,999
1,003	8,998

Hour	COUNTDOWN
1,004	8,997
1,005	8,996
1,006	8,995
1,007	8,994
1,008	8,993
1,009	8,992
1,010	8,991
1,011	8,990
1,012	8,989
1,013	8,988
1,014	8,987
1,015	8,986
1,016	8,985
1,017	8,984
1,018	8,983
1,019	8,982
1,020	8,981

Hour	COUNTDOWN
1,021	8,980
1,022	8,979
1,023	8,978
1,024	8,977
1,025	8,976
1,026	8,975
1,027	8,974
1,028	8,973
1,029	8,972
1,030	8,971
1,031	8,970
1,032	8,969
1,033	8,968
1,034	8,967
1,035	8,966
1,036	8,965
1,037	8,964

Hour	COUNTDOWN
1,038	8,963
1,039	8,962
1,040	8,961
1,041	8,960
1,042	8,959
1,043	8,958
1,044	8,957
1,045	8,956
1,046	8,955
1,047	8,954
1,048	8,953
1,049	8,952
1,050	8,951
1,051	8,950
1,052	8,949
1,053	8,948
1,054	8,947

Hour	COUNTDOWN
1,055	8,946
1,056	8,945
1,057	8,944
1,058	8,943
1,059	8,942
1,060	8,941
1,061	8,940
1,062	8,939
1,063	8,938
1,064	8,937
1,065	8,936
1,066	8,935
1,067	8,934
1,068	8,933
1,069	8,932
1,070	8,931
1,071	8,930

Hour	COUNTDOWN
1,072	8,929
1,073	8,928
1,074	8,927
1,075	8,926
1,076	8,925
1,077	8,924
1,078	8,923
1,079	8,922
1,080	8,921
1,081	8,920
1,082	8,919
1,083	8,918
1,084	8,917
1,085	8,916
1,086	8,915
1,087	8,914
1,088	8,913

Hour	COUNTDOWN
1,089	8,912
1,090	8,911
1,091	8,910
1,092	8,909
1,093	8,908
1,094	8,907
1,095	8,906
1,096	8,905
1,097	8,904
1,098	8,903
1,099	8,902
1,100	8,901
1,101	8,900
1,102	8,899
1,103	8,898
1,104	8,897
1,105	8,896

Hour	COUNTDOWN
1,106	8,895
1,107	8,894
1,108	8,893
1,109	8,892
1,110	8,891
1,111	8,890
1,112	8,889
1,113	8,888
1,114	8,887
1,115	8,886
1,116	8,885
1,117	8,884
1,118	8,883
1,119	8,882
1,120	8,881
1,121	8,880
1,122	8,879

Hour	COUNTDOWN
1,123	8,878
1,124	8,877
1,125	8,876
1,126	8,875
1,127	8,874
1,128	8,873
1,129	8,872
1,130	8,871
1,131	8,870
1,132	8,869
1,133	8,868
1,134	8,867
1,135	8,866
1,136	8,865
1,137	8,864
1,138	8,863
1,139	8,862

Hour	COUNTDOWN
1,140	8,861
1,141	8,860
1,142	8,859
1,143	8,858
1,144	8,857
1,145	8,856
1,146	8,855
1,147	8,854
1,148	8,853
1,149	8,852
1,150	8,851
1,151	8,850
1,152	8,849
1,153	8,848
1,154	8,847
1,155	8,846
1,156	8,845

Hour	COUNTDOWN
1,157	8,844
1,158	8,843
1,159	8,842
1,160	8,841
1,161	8,840
1,162	8,839
1,163	8,838
1,164	8,837
1,165	8,836
1,166	8,835
1,167	8,834
1,168	8,833
1,169	8,832
1,170	8,831
1,171	8,830
1,172	8,829
1,173	8,828

Hour	COUNTDOWN
1,174	8,827
1,175	8,826
1,176	8,825
1,177	8,824
1,178	8,823
1,179	8,822
1,180	8,821
1,181	8,820
1,182	8,819
1,183	8,818
1,184	8,817
1,185	8,816
1,186	8,815
1,187	8,814
1,188	8,813
1,189	8,812
1,190	8,811

Hour	COUNTDOWN
1,191	8,810
1,192	8,809
1,193	8,808
1,194	8,807
1,195	8,806
1,196	8,805
1,197	8,804
1,198	8,803
1,199	8,802
1,200	8,801
1,201	8,800
1,202	8,799
1,203	8,798
1,204	8,797
1,205	8,796
1,206	8,795
1,207	8,794

Hour	COUNTDOWN
1,208	8,793
1,209	8,792
1,210	8,791
1,211	8,790
1,212	8,789
1,213	8,788
1,214	8,787
1,215	8,786
1,216	8,785
1,217	8,784
1,218	8,783
1,219	8,782
1,220	8,781
1,221	8,780
1,222	8,779
1,223	8,778
1,224	8,777

Hour	COUNTDOWN
1,225	8,776
1,226	8,775
1,227	8,774
1,228	8,773
1,229	8,772
1,230	8,771
1,231	8,770
1,232	8,769
1,233	8,768
1,234	8,767
1,235	8,766
1,236	8,765
1,237	8,764
1,238	8,763
1,239	8,762
1,240	8,761
1,241	8,760

Hour	COUNTDOWN
1,242	8,759
1,243	8,758
1,244	8,757
1,245	8,756
1,246	8,755
1,247	8,754
1,248	8,753
1,249	8,752
1,250	8,751
1,251	8,750
1,252	8,749
1,253	8,748
1,254	8,747
1,255	8,746
1,256	8,745
1,257	8,744
1,258	8,743

Hour	COUNTDOWN
1,259	8,742
1,260	8,741
1,261	8,740
1,262	8,739
1,263	8,738
1,264	8,737
1,265	8,736
1,266	8,735
1,267	8,734
1,268	8,733
1,269	8,732
1,270	8,731
1,271	8,730
1,272	8,729
1,273	8,728
1,274	8,727
1,275	8,726

Hour	COUNTDOWN
1,276	8,725
1,277	8,724
1,278	8,723
1,279	8,722
1,280	8,721
1,281	8,720
1,282	8,719
1,283	8,718
1,284	8,717
1,285	8,716
1,286	8,715
1,287	8,714
1,288	8,713
1,289	8,712
1,290	8,711
1,291	8,710
1,292	8,709

Hour	COUNTDOWN
1,293	8,708
1,294	8,707
1,295	8,706
1,296	8,705
1,297	8,704
1,298	8,703
1,299	8,702
1,300	8,701
1,301	8,700
1,302	8,699
1,303	8,698
1,304	8,697
1,305	8,696
1,306	8,695
1,307	8,694
1,308	8,693
1,309	8,692

Hour	COUNTDOWN
1,310	8,691
1,311	8,690
1,312	8,689
1,313	8,688
1,314	8,687
1,315	8,686
1,316	8,685
1,317	8,684
1,318	8,683
1,319	8,682
1,320	8,681
1,321	8,680
1,322	8,679
1,323	8,678
1,324	8,677
1,325	8,676
1,326	8,675

Hour	COUNTDOWN
1,327	8,674
1,328	8,673
1,329	8,672
1,330	8,671
1,331	8,670
1,332	8,669
1,333	8,668
1,334	8,667
1,335	8,666
1,336	8,665
1,337	8,664
1,338	8,663
1,339	8,662
1,340	8,661
1,341	8,660
1,342	8,659
1,343	8,658

Hour	COUNTDOWN
1,344	8,657
1,345	8,656
1,346	8,655
1,347	8,654
1,348	8,653
1,349	8,652
1,350	8,651
1,351	8,650
1,352	8,649
1,353	8,648
1,354	8,647
1,355	8,646
1,356	8,645
1,357	8,644
1,358	8,643
1,359	8,642
1,360	8,641

Hour	COUNTDOWN
1,361	8,640
1,362	8,639
1,363	8,638
1,364	8,637
1,365	8,636
1,366	8,635
1,367	8,634
1,368	8,633
1,369	8,632
1,370	8,631
1,371	8,630
1,372	8,629
1,373	8,628
1,374	8,627
1,375	8,626
1,376	8,625
1,377	8,624

Hour	COUNTDOWN
1,378	8,623
1,379	8,622
1,380	8,621
1,381	8,620
1,382	8,619
1,383	8,618
1,384	8,617
1,385	8,616
1,386	8,615
1,387	8,614
1,388	8,613
1,389	8,612
1,390	8,611
1,391	8,610
1,392	8,609
1,393	8,608
1,394	8,607

Hour	COUNTDOWN
1,395	8,606
1,396	8,605
1,397	8,604
1,398	8,603
1,399	8,602
1,400	8,601
1,401	8,600
1,402	8,599
1,403	8,598
1,404	8,597
1,405	8,596
1,406	8,595
1,407	8,594
1,408	8,593
1,409	8,592
1,410	8,591
1,411	8,590

Hour	COUNTDOWN
1,412	8,589
1,413	8,588
1,414	8,587
1,415	8,586
1,416	8,585
1,417	8,584
1,418	8,583
1,419	8,582
1,420	8,581
1,421	8,580
1,422	8,579
1,423	8,578
1,424	8,577
1,425	8,576
1,426	8,575
1,427	8,574
1,428	8,573

Hour	COUNTDOWN
1,429	8,572
1,430	8,571
1,431	8,570
1,432	8,569
1,433	8,568
1,434	8,567
1,435	8,566
1,436	8,565
1,437	8,564
1,438	8,563
1,439	8,562
1,440	8,561
1,441	8,560
1,442	8,559
1,443	8,558
1,444	8,557
1,445	8,556

Hour	COUNTDOWN
1,446	8,555
1,447	8,554
1,448	8,553
1,449	8,552
1,450	8,551
1,451	8,550
1,452	8,549
1,453	8,548
1,454	8,547
1,455	8,546
1,456	8,545
1,457	8,544
1,458	8,543
1,459	8,542
1,460	8,541
1,461	8,540
1,462	8,539

Hour	COUNTDOWN
1,463	8,538
1,464	8,537
1,465	8,536
1,466	8,535
1,467	8,534
1,468	8,533
1,469	8,532
1,470	8,531
1,471	8,530
1,472	8,529
1,473	8,528
1,474	8,527
1,475	8,526
1,476	8,525
1,477	8,524
1,478	8,523
1,479	8,522

Hour	COUNTDOWN
1,480	8,521
1,481	8,520
1,482	8,519
1,483	8,518
1,484	8,517
1,485	8,516
1,486	8,515
1,487	8,514
1,488	8,513
1,489	8,512
1,490	8,511
1,491	8,510
1,492	8,509
1,493	8,508
1,494	8,507
1,495	8,506
1,496	8,505

Hour	COUNTDOWN
1,497	8,504
1,498	8,503
1,499	8,502
1,500	8,501
1,501	8,500
1,502	8,499
1,503	8,498
1,504	8,497
1,505	8,496
1,506	8,495
1,507	8,494
1,508	8,493
1,509	8,492
1,510	8,491
1,511	8,490
1,512	8,489
1,513	8,488

Hour	COUNTDOWN
1,514	8,487
1,515	8,486
1,516	8,485
1,517	8,484
1,518	8,483
1,519	8,482
1,520	8,481
1,521	8,480
1,522	8,479
1,523	8,478
1,524	8,477
1,525	8,476
1,526	8,475
1,527	8,474
1,528	8,473
1,529	8,472
1,530	8,471

Hour	COUNTDOWN
1,531	8,470
1,532	8,469
1,533	8,468
1,534	8,467
1,535	8,466
1,536	8,465
1,537	8,464
1,538	8,463
1,539	8,462
1,540	8,461
1,541	8,460
1,542	8,459
1,543	8,458
1,544	8,457
1,545	8,456
1,546	8,455
1,547	8,454

Hour	COUNTDOWN
1,548	8,453
1,549	8,452
1,550	8,451
1,551	8,450
1,552	8,449
1,553	8,448
1,554	8,447
1,555	8,446
1,556	8,445
1,557	8,444
1,558	8,443
1,559	8,442
1,560	8,441
1,561	8,440
1,562	8,439
1,563	8,438
1,564	8,437

Hour	COUNTDOWN
1,565	8,436
1,566	8,435
1,567	8,434
1,568	8,433
1,569	8,432
1,570	8,431
1,571	8,430
1,572	8,429
1,573	8,428
1,574	8,427
1,575	8,426
1,576	8,425
1,577	8,424
1,578	8,423
1,579	8,422
1,580	8,421
1,581	8,420

Hour	COUNTDOWN
1,582	8,419
1,583	8,418
1,584	8,417
1,585	8,416
1,586	8,415
1,587	8,414
1,588	8,413
1,589	8,412
1,590	8,411
1,591	8,410
1,592	8,409
1,593	8,408
1,594	8,407
1,595	8,406
1,596	8,405
1,597	8,404
1,598	8,403

Hour	COUNTDOWN
1,599	8,402
1,600	8,401
1,601	8,400
1,602	8,399
1,603	8,398
1,604	8,397
1,605	8,396
1,606	8,395
1,607	8,394
1,608	8,393
1,609	8,392
1,610	8,391
1,611	8,390
1,612	8,389
1,613	8,388
1,614	8,387
1,615	8,386

Hour	COUNTDOWN
1,616	8,385
1,617	8,384
1,618	8,383
1,619	8,382
1,620	8,381
1,621	8,380
1,622	8,379
1,623	8,378
1,624	8,377
1,625	8,376
1,626	8,375
1,627	8,374
1,628	8,373
1,629	8,372
1,630	8,371
1,631	8,370
1,632	8,369

Hour	COUNTDOWN
1,633	8,368
1,634	8,367
1,635	8,366
1,636	8,365
1,637	8,364
1,638	8,363
1,639	8,362
1,640	8,361
1,641	8,360
1,642	8,359
1,643	8,358
1,644	8,357
1,645	8,356
1,646	8,355
1,647	8,354
1,648	8,353
1,649	8,352

Hour	COUNTDOWN
1,650	8,351
1,651	8,350
1,652	8,349
1,653	8,348
1,654	8,347
1,655	8,346
1,656	8,345
1,657	8,344
1,658	8,343
1,659	8,342
1,660	8,341
1,661	8,340
1,662	8,339
1,663	8,338
1,664	8,337
1,665	8,336
1,666	8,335

Hour	COUNTDOWN
1,667	8,334
1,668	8,333
1,669	8,332
1,670	8,331
1,671	8,330
1,672	8,329
1,673	8,328
1,674	8,327
1,675	8,326
1,676	8,325
1,677	8,324
1,678	8,323
1,679	8,322
1,680	8,321
1,681	8,320
1,682	8,319
1,683	8,318

Hour	COUNTDOWN
1,684	8,317
1,685	8,316
1,686	8,315
1,687	8,314
1,688	8,313
1,689	8,312
1,690	8,311
1,691	8,310
1,692	8,309
1,693	8,308
1,694	8,307
1,695	8,306
1,696	8,305
1,697	8,304
1,698	8,303
1,699	8,302
1,700	8,301

Hour	COUNTDOWN
1,701	8,300
1,702	8,299
1,703	8,298
1,704	8,297
1,705	8,296
1,706	8,295
1,707	8,294
1,708	8,293
1,709	8,292
1,710	8,291
1,711	8,290
1,712	8,289
1,713	8,288
1,714	8,287
1,715	8,286
1,716	8,285
1,717	8,284

Hour	COUNTDOWN
1,718	8,283
1,719	8,282
1,720	8,281
1,721	8,280
1,722	8,279
1,723	8,278
1,724	8,277
1,725	8,276
1,726	8,275
1,727	8,274
1,728	8,273
1,729	8,272
1,730	8,271
1,731	8,270
1,732	8,269
1,733	8,268
1,734	8,267

Hour	COUNTDOWN
1,735	8,266
1,736	8,265
1,737	8,264
1,738	8,263
1,739	8,262
1,740	8,261
1,741	8,260
1,742	8,259
1,743	8,258
1,744	8,257
1,745	8,256
1,746	8,255
1,747	8,254
1,748	8,253
1,749	8,252
1,750	8,251
1,751	8,250

Hour	COUNTDOWN
1,752	8,249
1,753	8,248
1,754	8,247
1,755	8,246
1,756	8,245
1,757	8,244
1,758	8,243
1,759	8,242
1,760	8,241
1,761	8,240
1,762	8,239
1,763	8,238
1,764	8,237
1,765	8,236
1,766	8,235
1,767	8,234
1,768	8,233

Hour	COUNTDOWN
1,769	8,232
1,770	8,231
1,771	8,230
1,772	8,229
1,773	8,228
1,774	8,227
1,775	8,226
1,776	8,225
1,777	8,224
1,778	8,223
1,779	8,222
1,780	8,221
1,781	8,220
1,782	8,219
1,783	8,218
1,784	8,217
1,785	8,216

Hour	COUNTDOWN
1,786	8,215
1,787	8,214
1,788	8,213
1,789	8,212
1,790	8,211
1,791	8,210
1,792	8,209
1,793	8,208
1,794	8,207
1,795	8,206
1,796	8,205
1,797	8,204
1,798	8,203
1,799	8,202
1,800	8,201
1,801	8,200
1,802	8,199

Hour	COUNTDOWN
1,803	8,198
1,804	8,197
1,805	8,196
1,806	8,195
1,807	8,194
1,808	8,193
1,809	8,192
1,810	8,191
1,811	8,190
1,812	8,189
1,813	8,188
1,814	8,187
1,815	8,186
1,816	8,185
1,817	8,184
1,818	8,183
1,819	8,182

Hour	COUNTDOWN
1,820	8,181
1,821	8,180
1,822	8,179
1,823	8,178
1,824	8,177
1,825	8,176
1,826	8,175
1,827	8,174
1,828	8,173
1,829	8,172
1,830	8,171
1,831	8,170
1,832	8,169
1,833	8,168
1,834	8,167
1,835	8,166
1,836	8,165

Hour	COUNTDOWN
1,837	8,164
1,838	8,163
1,839	8,162
1,840	8,161
1,841	8,160
1,842	8,159
1,843	8,158
1,844	8,157
1,845	8,156
1,846	8,155
1,847	8,154
1,848	8,153
1,849	8,152
1,850	8,151
1,851	8,150
1,852	8,149
1,853	8,148

Hour	COUNTDOWN
1,854	8,147
1,855	8,146
1,856	8,145
1,857	8,144
1,858	8,143
1,859	8,142
1,860	8,141
1,861	8,140
1,862	8,139
1,863	8,138
1,864	8,137
1,865	8,136
1,866	8,135
1,867	8,134
1,868	8,133
1,869	8,132
1,870	8,131

Hour	COUNTDOWN
1,871	8,130
1,872	8,129
1,873	8,128
1,874	8,127
1,875	8,126
1,876	8,125
1,877	8,124
1,878	8,123
1,879	8,122
1,880	8,121
1,881	8,120
1,882	8,119
1,883	8,118
1,884	8,117
1,885	8,116
1,886	8,115
1,887	8,114

Hour	COUNTDOWN
1,888	8,113
1,889	8,112
1,890	8,111
1,891	8,110
1,892	8,109
1,893	8,108
1,894	8,107
1,895	8,106
1,896	8,105
1,897	8,104
1,898	8,103
1,899	8,102
1,900	8,101
1,901	8,100
1,902	8,099
1,903	8,098
1,904	8,097

Hour	COUNTDOWN
1,905	8,096
1,906	8,095
1,907	8,094
1,908	8,093
1,909	8,092
1,910	8,091
1,911	8,090
1,912	8,089
1,913	8,088
1,914	8,087
1,915	8,086
1,916	8,085
1,917	8,084
1,918	8,083
1,919	8,082
1,920	8,081
1,921	8,080

Hour	COUNTDOWN
1,922	8,079
1,923	8,078
1,924	8,077
1,925	8,076
1,926	8,075
1,927	8,074
1,928	8,073
1,929	8,072
1,930	8,071
1,931	8,070
1,932	8,069
1,933	8,068
1,934	8,067
1,935	8,066
1,936	8,065
1,937	8,064
1,938	8,063

Hour	COUNTDOWN
1,939	8,062
1,940	8,061
1,941	8,060
1,942	8,059
1,943	8,058
1,944	8,057
1,945	8,056
1,946	8,055
1,947	8,054
1,948	8,053
1,949	8,052
1,950	8,051
1,951	8,050
1,952	8,049
1,953	8,048
1,954	8,047
1,955	8,046

Hour	COUNTDOWN
1,956	8,045
1,957	8,044
1,958	8,043
1,959	8,042
1,960	8,041
1,961	8,040
1,962	8,039
1,963	8,038
1,964	8,037
1,965	8,036
1,966	8,035
1,967	8,034
1,968	8,033
1,969	8,032
1,970	8,031
1,971	8,030
1,972	8,029

Hour	COUNTDOWN
1,973	8,028
1,974	8,027
1,975	8,026
1,976	8,025
1,977	8,024
1,978	8,023
1,979	8,022
1,980	8,021
1,981	8,020
1,982	8,019
1,983	8,018
1,984	8,017
1,985	8,016
1,986	8,015
1,987	8,014
1,988	8,013
1,989	8,012

Hour	COUNTDOWN
1,990	8,011
1,991	8,010
1,992	8,009
1,993	8,008
1,994	8,007
1,995	8,006
1,996	8,005
1,997	8,004
1,998	8,003
1,999	8,002
2,000	8,001
2,001	8,000
2,002	7,999
2,003	7,998
2,004	7,997
2,005	7,996
2,006	7,995

Hour	COUNTDOWN
2,007	7,994
2,008	7,993
2,009	7,992
2,010	7,991
2,011	7,990
2,012	7,989
2,013	7,988
2,014	7,987
2,015	7,986
2,016	7,985
2,017	7,984
2,018	7,983
2,019	7,982
2,020	7,981
2,021	7,980
2,022	7,979
2,023	7,978

Hour	COUNTDOWN
2,024	7,977
2,025	7,976
2,026	7,975
2,027	7,974
2,028	7,973
2,029	7,972
2,030	7,971
2,031	7,970
2,032	7,969
2,033	7,968
2,034	7,967
2,035	7,966
2,036	7,965
2,037	7,964
2,038	7,963
2,039	7,962
2,040	7,961

Hour	COUNTDOWN
2,041	7,960
2,042	7,959
2,043	7,958
2,044	7,957
2,045	7,956
2,046	7,955
2,047	7,954
2,048	7,953
2,049	7,952
2,050	7,951
2,051	7,950
2,052	7,949
2,053	7,948
2,054	7,947
2,055	7,946
2,056	7,945
2,057	7,944

Hour	COUNTDOWN
2,058	7,943
2,059	7,942
2,060	7,941
2,061	7,940
2,062	7,939
2,063	7,938
2,064	7,937
2,065	7,936
2,066	7,935
2,067	7,934
2,068	7,933
2,069	7,932
2,070	7,931
2,071	7,930
2,072	7,929
2,073	7,928
2,074	7,927

Hour	COUNTDOWN
2,075	7,926
2,076	7,925
2,077	7,924
2,078	7,923
2,079	7,922
2,080	7,921
2,081	7,920
2,082	7,919
2,083	7,918
2,084	7,917
2,085	7,916
2,086	7,915
2,087	7,914
2,088	7,913
2,089	7,912
2,090	7,911
2,091	7,910

Hour	COUNTDOWN
2,092	7,909
2,093	7,908
2,094	7,907
2,095	7,906
2,096	7,905
2,097	7,904
2,098	7,903
2,099	7,902
2,100	7,901
2,101	7,900
2,102	7,899
2,103	7,898
2,104	7,897
2,105	7,896
2,106	7,895
2,107	7,894
2,108	7,893

Hour	COUNTDOWN
2,109	7,892
2,110	7,891
2,111	7,890
2,112	7,889
2,113	7,888
2,114	7,887
2,115	7,886
2,116	7,885
2,117	7,884
2,118	7,883
2,119	7,882
2,120	7,881
2,121	7,880
2,122	7,879
2,123	7,878
2,124	7,877
2,125	7,876

Hour	COUNTDOWN
2,126	7,875
2,127	7,874
2,128	7,873
2,129	7,872
2,130	7,871
2,131	7,870
2,132	7,869
2,133	7,868
2,134	7,867
2,135	7,866
2,136	7,865
2,137	7,864
2,138	7,863
2,139	7,862
2,140	7,861
2,141	7,860
2,142	7,859

Hour	COUNTDOWN
2,143	7,858
2,144	7,857
2,145	7,856
2,146	7,855
2,147	7,854
2,148	7,853
2,149	7,852
2,150	7,851
2,151	7,850
2,152	7,849
2,153	7,848
2,154	7,847
2,155	7,846
2,156	7,845
2,157	7,844
2,158	7,843
2,159	7,842

Hour	COUNTDOWN
2,160	7,841
2,161	7,840
2,162	7,839
2,163	7,838
2,164	7,837
2,165	7,836
2,166	7,835
2,167	7,834
2,168	7,833
2,169	7,832
2,170	7,831
2,171	7,830
2,172	7,829
2,173	7,828
2,174	7,827
2,175	7,826
2,176	7,825

Hour	COUNTDOWN
2,177	7,824
2,178	7,823
2,179	7,822
2,180	7,821
2,181	7,820
2,182	7,819
2,183	7,818
2,184	7,817
2,185	7,816
2,186	7,815
2,187	7,814
2,188	7,813
2,189	7,812
2,190	7,811
2,191	7,810
2,192	7,809
2,193	7,808

Hour	COUNTDOWN
2,194	7,807
2,195	7,806
2,196	7,805
2,197	7,804
2,198	7,803
2,199	7,802
2,200	7,801
2,201	7,800
2,202	7,799
2,203	7,798
2,204	7,797
2,205	7,796
2,206	7,795
2,207	7,794
2,208	7,793
2,209	7,792
2,210	7,791

Hour	COUNTDOWN
2,211	7,790
2,212	7,789
2,213	7,788
2,214	7,787
2,215	7,786
2,216	7,785
2,217	7,784
2,218	7,783
2,219	7,782
2,220	7,781
2,221	7,780
2,222	7,779
2,223	7,778
2,224	7,777
2,225	7,776
2,226	7,775
2,227	7,774

Hour	COUNTDOWN
2,228	7,773
2,229	7,772
2,230	7,771
2,231	7,770
2,232	7,769
2,233	7,768
2,234	7,767
2,235	7,766
2,236	7,765
2,237	7,764
2,238	7,763
2,239	7,762
2,240	7,761
2,241	7,760
2,242	7,759
2,243	7,758
2,244	7,757

Hour	COUNTDOWN
2,245	7,756
2,246	7,755
2,247	7,754
2,248	7,753
2,249	7,752
2,250	7,751
2,251	7,750
2,252	7,749
2,253	7,748
2,254	7,747
2,255	7,746
2,256	7,745
2,257	7,744
2,258	7,743
2,259	7,742
2,260	7,741
2,261	7,740

Hour	COUNTDOWN
2,262	7,739
2,263	7,738
2,264	7,737
2,265	7,736
2,266	7,735
2,267	7,734
2,268	7,733
2,269	7,732
2,270	7,731
2,271	7,730
2,272	7,729
2,273	7,728
2,274	7,727
2,275	7,726
2,276	7,725
2,277	7,724
2,278	7,723

Hour	COUNTDOWN
2,279	7,722
2,280	7,721
2,281	7,720
2,282	7,719
2,283	7,718
2,284	7,717
2,285	7,716
2,286	7,715
2,287	7,714
2,288	7,713
2,289	7,712
2,290	7,711
2,291	7,710
2,292	7,709
2,293	7,708
2,294	7,707
2,295	7,706

Hour	COUNTDOWN
2,296	7,705
2,297	7,704
2,298	7,703
2,299	7,702
2,300	7,701
2,301	7,700
2,302	7,699
2,303	7,698
2,304	7,697
2,305	7,696
2,306	7,695
2,307	7,694
2,308	7,693
2,309	7,692
2,310	7,691
2,311	7,690
2,312	7,689

Hour	COUNTDOWN
2,313	7,688
2,314	7,687
2,315	7,686
2,316	7,685
2,317	7,684
2,318	7,683
2,319	7,682
2,320	7,681
2,321	7,680
2,322	7,679
2,323	7,678
2,324	7,677
2,325	7,676
2,326	7,675
2,327	7,674
2,328	7,673
2,329	7,672

Hour	COUNTDOWN
2,330	7,671
2,331	7,670
2,332	7,669
2,333	7,668
2,334	7,667
2,335	7,666
2,336	7,665
2,337	7,664
2,338	7,663
2,339	7,662
2,340	7,661
2,341	7,660
2,342	7,659
2,343	7,658
2,344	7,657
2,345	7,656
2,346	7,655

Hour	COUNTDOWN
2,347	7,654
2,348	7,653
2,349	7,652
2,350	7,651
2,351	7,650
2,352	7,649
2,353	7,648
2,354	7,647
2,355	7,646
2,356	7,645
2,357	7,644
2,358	7,643
2,359	7,642
2,360	7,641
2,361	7,640
2,362	7,639
2,363	7,638

Hour	COUNTDOWN
2,364	7,637
2,365	7,636
2,366	7,635
2,367	7,634
2,368	7,633
2,369	7,632
2,370	7,631
2,371	7,630
2,372	7,629
2,373	7,628
2,374	7,627
2,375	7,626
2,376	7,625
2,377	7,624
2,378	7,623
2,379	7,622
2,380	7,621

Hour	COUNTDOWN
2,381	7,620
2,382	7,619
2,383	7,618
2,384	7,617
2,385	7,616
2,386	7,615
2,387	7,614
2,388	7,613
2,389	7,612
2,390	7,611
2,391	7,610
2,392	7,609
2,393	7,608
2,394	7,607
2,395	7,606
2,396	7,605
2,397	7,604

Hour	COUNTDOWN
2,398	7,603
2,399	7,602
2,400	7,601
2,401	7,600
2,402	7,599
2,403	7,598
2,404	7,597
2,405	7,596
2,406	7,595
2,407	7,594
2,408	7,593
2,409	7,592
2,410	7,591
2,411	7,590
2,412	7,589
2,413	7,588
2,414	7,587

Hour	COUNTDOWN
2,415	7,586
2,416	7,585
2,417	7,584
2,418	7,583
2,419	7,582
2,420	7,581
2,421	7,580
2,422	7,579
2,423	7,578
2,424	7,577
2,425	7,576
2,426	7,575
2,427	7,574
2,428	7,573
2,429	7,572
2,430	7,571
2,431	7,570

Hour	COUNTDOWN
2,432	7,569
2,433	7,568
2,434	7,567
2,435	7,566
2,436	7,565
2,437	7,564
2,438	7,563
2,439	7,562
2,440	7,561
2,441	7,560
2,442	7,559
2,443	7,558
2,444	7,557
2,445	7,556
2,446	7,555
2,447	7,554
2,448	7,553

Hour	COUNTDOWN
2,449	7,552
2,450	7,551
2,451	7,550
2,452	7,549
2,453	7,548
2,454	7,547
2,455	7,546
2,456	7,545
2,457	7,544
2,458	7,543
2,459	7,542
2,460	7,541
2,461	7,540
2,462	7,539
2,463	7,538
2,464	7,537
2,465	7,536

Hour	COUNTDOWN
2,466	7,535
2,467	7,534
2,468	7,533
2,469	7,532
2,470	7,531
2,471	7,530
2,472	7,529
2,473	7,528
2,474	7,527
2,475	7,526
2,476	7,525
2,477	7,524
2,478	7,523
2,479	7,522
2,480	7,521
2,481	7,520
2,482	7,519

Hour	COUNTDOWN
2,483	7,518
2,484	7,517
2,485	7,516
2,486	7,515
2,487	7,514
2,488	7,513
2,489	7,512
2,490	7,511
2,491	7,510
2,492	7,509
2,493	7,508
2,494	7,507
2,495	7,506
2,496	7,505
2,497	7,504
2,498	7,503
2,499	7,502

Hour	COUNTDOWN
2,500	7,501
2,501	7,500
2,502	7,499
2,503	7,498
2,504	7,497
2,505	7,496
2,506	7,495
2,507	7,494
2,508	7,493
2,509	7,492
2,510	7,491
2,511	7,490
2,512	7,489
2,513	7,488
2,514	7,487
2,515	7,486
2,516	7,485

Hour	COUNTDOWN
2,517	7,484
2,518	7,483
2,519	7,482
2,520	7,481
2,521	7,480
2,522	7,479
2,523	7,478
2,524	7,477
2,525	7,476
2,526	7,475
2,527	7,474
2,528	7,473
2,529	7,472
2,530	7,471
2,531	7,470
2,532	7,469
2,533	7,468

Hour	COUNTDOWN
2,534	7,467
2,535	7,466
2,536	7,465
2,537	7,464
2,538	7,463
2,539	7,462
2,540	7,461
2,541	7,460
2,542	7,459
2,543	7,458
2,544	7,457
2,545	7,456
2,546	7,455
2,547	7,454
2,548	7,453
2,549	7,452
2,550	7,451

Hour	COUNTDOWN
2,551	7,450
2,552	7,449
2,553	7,448
2,554	7,447
2,555	7,446
2,556	7,445
2,557	7,444
2,558	7,443
2,559	7,442
2,560	7,441
2,561	7,440
2,562	7,439
2,563	7,438
2,564	7,437
2,565	7,436
2,566	7,435
2,567	7,434

Hour	COUNTDOWN
2,568	7,433
2,569	7,432
2,570	7,431
2,571	7,430
2,572	7,429
2,573	7,428
2,574	7,427
2,575	7,426
2,576	7,425
2,577	7,424
2,578	7,423
2,579	7,422
2,580	7,421
2,581	7,420
2,582	7,419
2,583	7,418
2,584	7,417

Hour	COUNTDOWN
2,585	7,416
2,586	7,415
2,587	7,414
2,588	7,413
2,589	7,412
2,590	7,411
2,591	7,410
2,592	7,409
2,593	7,408
2,594	7,407
2,595	7,406
2,596	7,405
2,597	7,404
2,598	7,403
2,599	7,402
2,600	7,401
2,601	7,400

Hour	COUNTDOWN
2,602	7,399
2,603	7,398
2,604	7,397
2,605	7,396
2,606	7,395
2,607	7,394
2,608	7,393
2,609	7,392
2,610	7,391
2,611	7,390
2,612	7,389
2,613	7,388
2,614	7,387
2,615	7,386
2,616	7,385
2,617	7,384
2,618	7,383

Hour	COUNTDOWN
2,619	7,382
2,620	7,381
2,621	7,380
2,622	7,379
2,623	7,378
2,624	7,377
2,625	7,376
2,626	7,375
2,627	7,374
2,628	7,373
2,629	7,372
2,630	7,371
2,631	7,370
2,632	7,369
2,633	7,368
2,634	7,367
2,635	7,366

Hour	COUNTDOWN
2,636	7,365
2,637	7,364
2,638	7,363
2,639	7,362
2,640	7,361
2,641	7,360
2,642	7,359
2,643	7,358
2,644	7,357
2,645	7,356
2,646	7,355
2,647	7,354
2,648	7,353
2,649	7,352
2,650	7,351
2,651	7,350
2,652	7,349

Hour	COUNTDOWN
2,653	7,348
2,654	7,347
2,655	7,346
2,656	7,345
2,657	7,344
2,658	7,343
2,659	7,342
2,660	7,341
2,661	7,340
2,662	7,339
2,663	7,338
2,664	7,337
2,665	7,336
2,666	7,335
2,667	7,334
2,668	7,333
2,669	7,332

Hour	COUNTDOWN
2,670	7,331
2,671	7,330
2,672	7,329
2,673	7,328
2,674	7,327
2,675	7,326
2,676	7,325
2,677	7,324
2,678	7,323
2,679	7,322
2,680	7,321
2,681	7,320
2,682	7,319
2,683	7,318
2,684	7,317
2,685	7,316
2,686	7,315

Hour	COUNTDOWN
2,687	7,314
2,688	7,313
2,689	7,312
2,690	7,311
2,691	7,310
2,692	7,309
2,693	7,308
2,694	7,307
2,695	7,306
2,696	7,305
2,697	7,304
2,698	7,303
2,699	7,302
2,700	7,301
2,701	7,300
2,702	7,299
2,703	7,298

Hour	COUNTDOWN
2,704	7,297
2,705	7,296
2,706	7,295
2,707	7,294
2,708	7,293
2,709	7,292
2,710	7,291
2,711	7,290
2,712	7,289
2,713	7,288
2,714	7,287
2,715	7,286
2,716	7,285
2,717	7,284
2,718	7,283
2,719	7,282
2,720	7,281

Hour	COUNTDOWN
2,721	7,280
2,722	7,279
2,723	7,278
2,724	7,277
2,725	7,276
2,726	7,275
2,727	7,274
2,728	7,273
2,729	7,272
2,730	7,271
2,731	7,270
2,732	7,269
2,733	7,268
2,734	7,267
2,735	7,266
2,736	7,265
2,737	7,264

Hour	COUNTDOWN
2,738	7,263
2,739	7,262
2,740	7,261
2,741	7,260
2,742	7,259
2,743	7,258
2,744	7,257
2,745	7,256
2,746	7,255
2,747	7,254
2,748	7,253
2,749	7,252
2,750	7,251
2,751	7,250
2,752	7,249
2,753	7,248
2,754	7,247

Hour	COUNTDOWN
2,755	7,246
2,756	7,245
2,757	7,244
2,758	7,243
2,759	7,242
2,760	7,241
2,761	7,240
2,762	7,239
2,763	7,238
2,764	7,237
2,765	7,236
2,766	7,235
2,767	7,234
2,768	7,233
2,769	7,232
2,770	7,231
2,771	7,230

Hour	COUNTDOWN
2,772	7,229
2,773	7,228
2,774	7,227
2,775	7,226
2,776	7,225
2,777	7,224
2,778	7,223
2,779	7,222
2,780	7,221
2,781	7,220
2,782	7,219
2,783	7,218
2,784	7,217
2,785	7,216
2,786	7,215
2,787	7,214
2,788	7,213

Hour	COUNTDOWN
2,789	7,212
2,790	7,211
2,791	7,210
2,792	7,209
2,793	7,208
2,794	7,207
2,795	7,206
2,796	7,205
2,797	7,204
2,798	7,203
2,799	7,202
2,800	7,201
2,801	7,200
2,802	7,199
2,803	7,198
2,804	7,197
2,805	7,196

Hour	COUNTDOWN
2,806	7,195
2,807	7,194
2,808	7,193
2,809	7,192
2,810	7,191
2,811	7,190
2,812	7,189
2,813	7,188
2,814	7,187
2,815	7,186
2,816	7,185
2,817	7,184
2,818	7,183
2,819	7,182
2,820	7,181
2,821	7,180
2,822	7,179

Hour	COUNTDOWN
2,823	7,178
2,824	7,177
2,825	7,176
2,826	7,175
2,827	7,174
2,828	7,173
2,829	7,172
2,830	7,171
2,831	7,170
2,832	7,169
2,833	7,168
2,834	7,167
2,835	7,166
2,836	7,165
2,837	7,164
2,838	7,163
2,839	7,162

Hour	COUNTDOWN
2,840	7,161
2,841	7,160
2,842	7,159
2,843	7,158
2,844	7,157
2,845	7,156
2,846	7,155
2,847	7,154
2,848	7,153
2,849	7,152
2,850	7,151
2,851	7,150
2,852	7,149
2,853	7,148
2,854	7,147
2,855	7,146
2,856	7,145

Hour	COUNTDOWN
2,857	7,144
2,858	7,143
2,859	7,142
2,860	7,141
2,861	7,140
2,862	7,139
2,863	7,138
2,864	7,137
2,865	7,136
2,866	7,135
2,867	7,134
2,868	7,133
2,869	7,132
2,870	7,131
2,871	7,130
2,872	7,129
2,873	7,128

Hour	COUNTDOWN
2,874	7,127
2,875	7,126
2,876	7,125
2,877	7,124
2,878	7,123
2,879	7,122
2,880	7,121
2,881	7,120
2,882	7,119
2,883	7,118
2,884	7,117
2,885	7,116
2,886	7,115
2,887	7,114
2,888	7,113
2,889	7,112
2,890	7,111

Hour	COUNTDOWN
2,891	7,110
2,892	7,109
2,893	7,108
2,894	7,107
2,895	7,106
2,896	7,105
2,897	7,104
2,898	7,103
2,899	7,102
2,900	7,101
2,901	7,100
2,902	7,099
2,903	7,098
2,904	7,097
2,905	7,096
2,906	7,095
2,907	7,094

Hour	COUNTDOWN
2,908	7,093
2,909	7,092
2,910	7,091
2,911	7,090
2,912	7,089
2,913	7,088
2,914	7,087
2,915	7,086
2,916	7,085
2,917	7,084
2,918	7,083
2,919	7,082
2,920	7,081
2,921	7,080
2,922	7,079
2,923	7,078
2,924	7,077

Hour	COUNTDOWN
2,925	7,076
2,926	7,075
2,927	7,074
2,928	7,073
2,929	7,072
2,930	7,071
2,931	7,070
2,932	7,069
2,933	7,068
2,934	7,067
2,935	7,066
2,936	7,065
2,937	7,064
2,938	7,063
2,939	7,062
2,940	7,061
2,941	7,060

Hour	COUNTDOWN
2,942	7,059
2,943	7,058
2,944	7,057
2,945	7,056
2,946	7,055
2,947	7,054
2,948	7,053
2,949	7,052
2,950	7,051
2,951	7,050
2,952	7,049
2,953	7,048
2,954	7,047
2,955	7,046
2,956	7,045
2,957	7,044
2,958	7,043

Hour	COUNTDOWN
2,959	7,042
2,960	7,041
2,961	7,040
2,962	7,039
2,963	7,038
2,964	7,037
2,965	7,036
2,966	7,035
2,967	7,034
2,968	7,033
2,969	7,032
2,970	7,031
2,971	7,030
2,972	7,029
2,973	7,028
2,974	7,027
2,975	7,026

Hour	COUNTDOWN
2,976	7,025
2,977	7,024
2,978	7,023
2,979	7,022
2,980	7,021
2,981	7,020
2,982	7,019
2,983	7,018
2,984	7,017
2,985	7,016
2,986	7,015
2,987	7,014
2,988	7,013
2,989	7,012
2,990	7,011
2,991	7,010
2,992	7,009

Hour	COUNTDOWN
2,993	7,008
2,994	7,007
2,995	7,006
2,996	7,005
2,997	7,004
2,998	7,003
2,999	7,002
3,000	7,001
3,001	7,000
3,002	6,999
3,003	6,998
3,004	6,997
3,005	6,996
3,006	6,995
3,007	6,994
3,008	6,993
3,009	6,992

Hour	COUNTDOWN
3,010	6,991
3,011	6,990
3,012	6,989
3,013	6,988
3,014	6,987
3,015	6,986
3,016	6,985
3,017	6,984
3,018	6,983
3,019	6,982
3,020	6,981
3,021	6,980
3,022	6,979
3,023	6,978
3,024	6,977
3,025	6,976
3,026	6,975

Hour	COUNTDOWN
3,027	6,974
3,028	6,973
3,029	6,972
3,030	6,971
3,031	6,970
3,032	6,969
3,033	6,968
3,034	6,967
3,035	6,966
3,036	6,965
3,037	6,964
3,038	6,963
3,039	6,962
3,040	6,961
3,041	6,960
3,042	6,959
3,043	6,958

Hour	COUNTDOWN
3,044	6,957
3,045	6,956
3,046	6,955
3,047	6,954
3,048	6,953
3,049	6,952
3,050	6,951
3,051	6,950
3,052	6,949
3,053	6,948
3,054	6,947
3,055	6,946
3,056	6,945
3,057	6,944
3,058	6,943
3,059	6,942
3,060	6,941

Hour	COUNTDOWN
3,061	6,940
3,062	6,939
3,063	6,938
3,064	6,937
3,065	6,936
3,066	6,935
3,067	6,934
3,068	6,933
3,069	6,932
3,070	6,931
3,071	6,930
3,072	6,929
3,073	6,928
3,074	6,927
3,075	6,926
3,076	6,925
3,077	6,924

Hour	COUNTDOWN
3,078	6,923
3,079	6,922
3,080	6,921
3,081	6,920
3,082	6,919
3,083	6,918
3,084	6,917
3,085	6,916
3,086	6,915
3,087	6,914
3,088	6,913
3,089	6,912
3,090	6,911
3,091	6,910
3,092	6,909
3,093	6,908
3,094	6,907

Hour	COUNTDOWN
3,095	6,906
3,096	6,905
3,097	6,904
3,098	6,903
3,099	6,902
3,100	6,901
3,101	6,900
3,102	6,899
3,103	6,898
3,104	6,897
3,105	6,896
3,106	6,895
3,107	6,894
3,108	6,893
3,109	6,892
3,110	6,891
3,111	6,890

Hour	COUNTDOWN
3,112	6,889
3,113	6,888
3,114	6,887
3,115	6,886
3,116	6,885
3,117	6,884
3,118	6,883
3,119	6,882
3,120	6,881
3,121	6,880
3,122	6,879
3,123	6,878
3,124	6,877
3,125	6,876
3,126	6,875
3,127	6,874
3,128	6,873

Hour	COUNTDOWN
3,129	6,872
3,130	6,871
3,131	6,870
3,132	6,869
3,133	6,868
3,134	6,867
3,135	6,866
3,136	6,865
3,137	6,864
3,138	6,863
3,139	6,862
3,140	6,861
3,141	6,860
3,142	6,859
3,143	6,858
3,144	6,857
3,145	6,856

Hour	COUNTDOWN
3,146	6,855
3,147	6,854
3,148	6,853
3,149	6,852
3,150	6,851
3,151	6,850
3,152	6,849
3,153	6,848
3,154	6,847
3,155	6,846
3,156	6,845
3,157	6,844
3,158	6,843
3,159	6,842
3,160	6,841
3,161	6,840
3,162	6,839

Hour	COUNTDOWN
3,163	6,838
3,164	6,837
3,165	6,836
3,166	6,835
3,167	6,834
3,168	6,833
3,169	6,832
3,170	6,831
3,171	6,830
3,172	6,829
3,173	6,828
3,174	6,827
3,175	6,826
3,176	6,825
3,177	6,824
3,178	6,823
3,179	6,822

Hour	COUNTDOWN
3,180	6,821
3,181	6,820
3,182	6,819
3,183	6,818
3,184	6,817
3,185	6,816
3,186	6,815
3,187	6,814
3,188	6,813
3,189	6,812
3,190	6,811
3,191	6,810
3,192	6,809
3,193	6,808
3,194	6,807
3,195	6,806
3,196	6,805

Hour	COUNTDOWN
3,197	6,804
3,198	6,803
3,199	6,802
3,200	6,801
3,201	6,800
3,202	6,799
3,203	6,798
3,204	6,797
3,205	6,796
3,206	6,795
3,207	6,794
3,208	6,793
3,209	6,792
3,210	6,791
3,211	6,790
3,212	6,789
3,213	6,788

Hour	COUNTDOWN
3,214	6,787
3,215	6,786
3,216	6,785
3,217	6,784
3,218	6,783
3,219	6,782
3,220	6,781
3,221	6,780
3,222	6,779
3,223	6,778
3,224	6,777
3,225	6,776
3,226	6,775
3,227	6,774
3,228	6,773
3,229	6,772
3,230	6,771

Hour	COUNTDOWN
3,231	6,770
3,232	6,769
3,233	6,768
3,234	6,767
3,235	6,766
3,236	6,765
3,237	6,764
3,238	6,763
3,239	6,762
3,240	6,761
3,241	6,760
3,242	6,759
3,243	6,758
3,244	6,757
3,245	6,756
3,246	6,755
3,247	6,754

Hour	COUNTDOWN
3,248	6,753
3,249	6,752
3,250	6,751
3,251	6,750
3,252	6,749
3,253	6,748
3,254	6,747
3,255	6,746
3,256	6,745
3,257	6,744
3,258	6,743
3,259	6,742
3,260	6,741
3,261	6,740
3,262	6,739
3,263	6,738
3,264	6,737

Hour	COUNTDOWN
3,265	6,736
3,266	6,735
3,267	6,734
3,268	6,733
3,269	6,732
3,270	6,731
3,271	6,730
3,272	6,729
3,273	6,728
3,274	6,727
3,275	6,726
3,276	6,725
3,277	6,724
3,278	6,723
3,279	6,722
3,280	6,721
3,281	6,720

Hour	COUNTDOWN
3,282	6,719
3,283	6,718
3,284	6,717
3,285	6,716
3,286	6,715
3,287	6,714
3,288	6,713
3,289	6,712
3,290	6,711
3,291	6,710
3,292	6,709
3,293	6,708
3,294	6,707
3,295	6,706
3,296	6,705
3,297	6,704
3,298	6,703

Hour	COUNTDOWN
3,299	6,702
3,300	6,701
3,301	6,700
3,302	6,699
3,303	6,698
3,304	6,697
3,305	6,696
3,306	6,695
3,307	6,694
3,308	6,693
3,309	6,692
3,310	6,691
3,311	6,690
3,312	6,689
3,313	6,688
3,314	6,687
3,315	6,686

Hour	COUNTDOWN
3,316	6,685
3,317	6,684
3,318	6,683
3,319	6,682
3,320	6,681
3,321	6,680
3,322	6,679
3,323	6,678
3,324	6,677
3,325	6,676
3,326	6,675
3,327	6,674
3,328	6,673
3,329	6,672
3,330	6,671
3,331	6,670
3,332	6,669

Hour	COUNTDOWN
3,333	6,668
3,334	6,667
3,335	6,666
3,336	6,665
3,337	6,664
3,338	6,663
3,339	6,662
3,340	6,661
3,341	6,660
3,342	6,659
3,343	6,658
3,344	6,657
3,345	6,656
3,346	6,655
3,347	6,654
3,348	6,653
3,349	6,652

Hour	COUNTDOWN
3,350	6,651
3,351	6,650
3,352	6,649
3,353	6,648
3,354	6,647
3,355	6,646
3,356	6,645
3,357	6,644
3,358	6,643
3,359	6,642
3,360	6,641
3,361	6,640
3,362	6,639
3,363	6,638
3,364	6,637
3,365	6,636
3,366	6,635

Hour	COUNTDOWN
3,367	6,634
3,368	6,633
3,369	6,632
3,370	6,631
3,371	6,630
3,372	6,629
3,373	6,628
3,374	6,627
3,375	6,626
3,376	6,625
3,377	6,624
3,378	6,623
3,379	6,622
3,380	6,621
3,381	6,620
3,382	6,619
3,383	6,618

Hour	COUNTDOWN
3,384	6,617
3,385	6,616
3,386	6,615
3,387	6,614
3,388	6,613
3,389	6,612
3,390	6,611
3,391	6,610
3,392	6,609
3,393	6,608
3,394	6,607
3,395	6,606
3,396	6,605
3,397	6,604
3,398	6,603
3,399	6,602
3,400	6,601

Hour	COUNTDOWN
3,401	6,600
3,402	6,599
3,403	6,598
3,404	6,597
3,405	6,596
3,406	6,595
3,407	6,594
3,408	6,593
3,409	6,592
3,410	6,591
3,411	6,590
3,412	6,589
3,413	6,588
3,414	6,587
3,415	6,586
3,416	6,585
3,417	6,584

Hour	COUNTDOWN
3,418	6,583
3,419	6,582
3,420	6,581
3,421	6,580
3,422	6,579
3,423	6,578
3,424	6,577
3,425	6,576
3,426	6,575
3,427	6,574
3,428	6,573
3,429	6,572
3,430	6,571
3,431	6,570
3,432	6,569
3,433	6,568
3,434	6,567

Hour	COUNTDOWN
3,435	6,566
3,436	6,565
3,437	6,564
3,438	6,563
3,439	6,562
3,440	6,561
3,441	6,560
3,442	6,559
3,443	6,558
3,444	6,557
3,445	6,556
3,446	6,555
3,447	6,554
3,448	6,553
3,449	6,552
3,450	6,551
3,451	6,550

Hour	COUNTDOWN
3,452	6,549
3,453	6,548
3,454	6,547
3,455	6,546
3,456	6,545
3,457	6,544
3,458	6,543
3,459	6,542
3,460	6,541
3,461	6,540
3,462	6,539
3,463	6,538
3,464	6,537
3,465	6,536
3,466	6,535
3,467	6,534
3,468	6,533

Hour	COUNTDOWN
3,469	6,532
3,470	6,531
3,471	6,530
3,472	6,529
3,473	6,528
3,474	6,527
3,475	6,526
3,476	6,525
3,477	6,524
3,478	6,523
3,479	6,522
3,480	6,521
3,481	6,520
3,482	6,519
3,483	6,518
3,484	6,517
3,485	6,516

Hour	COUNTDOWN
3,486	6,515
3,487	6,514
3,488	6,513
3,489	6,512
3,490	6,511
3,491	6,510
3,492	6,509
3,493	6,508
3,494	6,507
3,495	6,506
3,496	6,505
3,497	6,504
3,498	6,503
3,499	6,502
3,500	6,501
3,501	6,500
3,502	6,499

Hour	COUNTDOWN
3,503	6,498
3,504	6,497
3,505	6,496
3,506	6,495
3,507	6,494
3,508	6,493
3,509	6,492
3,510	6,491
3,511	6,490
3,512	6,489
3,513	6,488
3,514	6,487
3,515	6,486
3,516	6,485
3,517	6,484
3,518	6,483
3,519	6,482

Hour	COUNTDOWN
3,520	6,481
3,521	6,480
3,522	6,479
3,523	6,478
3,524	6,477
3,525	6,476
3,526	6,475
3,527	6,474
3,528	6,473
3,529	6,472
3,530	6,471
3,531	6,470
3,532	6,469
3,533	6,468
3,534	6,467
3,535	6,466
3,536	6,465

Hour	COUNTDOWN
3,537	6,464
3,538	6,463
3,539	6,462
3,540	6,461
3,541	6,460
3,542	6,459
3,543	6,458
3,544	6,457
3,545	6,456
3,546	6,455
3,547	6,454
3,548	6,453
3,549	6,452
3,550	6,451
3,551	6,450
3,552	6,449
3,553	6,448

Hour	COUNTDOWN
3,554	6,447
3,555	6,446
3,556	6,445
3,557	6,444
3,558	6,443
3,559	6,442
3,560	6,441
3,561	6,440
3,562	6,439
3,563	6,438
3,564	6,437
3,565	6,436
3,566	6,435
3,567	6,434
3,568	6,433
3,569	6,432
3,570	6,431

Hour	COUNTDOWN
3,571	6,430
3,572	6,429
3,573	6,428
3,574	6,427
3,575	6,426
3,576	6,425
3,577	6,424
3,578	6,423
3,579	6,422
3,580	6,421
3,581	6,420
3,582	6,419
3,583	6,418
3,584	6,417
3,585	6,416
3,586	6,415
3,587	6,414

Hour	COUNTDOWN
3,588	6,413
3,589	6,412
3,590	6,411
3,591	6,410
3,592	6,409
3,593	6,408
3,594	6,407
3,595	6,406
3,596	6,405
3,597	6,404
3,598	6,403
3,599	6,402
3,600	6,401
3,601	6,400
3,602	6,399
3,603	6,398
3,604	6,397

Hour	COUNTDOWN
3,605	6,396
3,606	6,395
3,607	6,394
3,608	6,393
3,609	6,392
3,610	6,391
3,611	6,390
3,612	6,389
3,613	6,388
3,614	6,387
3,615	6,386
3,616	6,385
3,617	6,384
3,618	6,383
3,619	6,382
3,620	6,381
3,621	6,380

Hour	COUNTDOWN
3,622	6,379
3,623	6,378
3,624	6,377
3,625	6,376
3,626	6,375
3,627	6,374
3,628	6,373
3,629	6,372
3,630	6,371
3,631	6,370
3,632	6,369
3,633	6,368
3,634	6,367
3,635	6,366
3,636	6,365
3,637	6,364
3,638	6,363

Hour	COUNTDOWN
3,639	6,362
3,640	6,361
3,641	6,360
3,642	6,359
3,643	6,358
3,644	6,357
3,645	6,356
3,646	6,355
3,647	6,354
3,648	6,353
3,649	6,352
3,650	6,351
3,651	6,350
3,652	6,349
3,653	6,348
3,654	6,347
3,655	6,346

Hour	COUNTDOWN
3,656	6,345
3,657	6,344
3,658	6,343
3,659	6,342
3,660	6,341
3,661	6,340
3,662	6,339
3,663	6,338
3,664	6,337
3,665	6,336
3,666	6,335
3,667	6,334
3,668	6,333
3,669	6,332
3,670	6,331
3,671	6,330
3,672	6,329

Hour	COUNTDOWN
3,673	6,328
3,674	6,327
3,675	6,326
3,676	6,325
3,677	6,324
3,678	6,323
3,679	6,322
3,680	6,321
3,681	6,320
3,682	6,319
3,683	6,318
3,684	6,317
3,685	6,316
3,686	6,315
3,687	6,314
3,688	6,313
3,689	6,312

Hour	COUNTDOWN
3,690	6,311
3,691	6,310
3,692	6,309
3,693	6,308
3,694	6,307
3,695	6,306
3,696	6,305
3,697	6,304
3,698	6,303
3,699	6,302
3,700	6,301
3,701	6,300
3,702	6,299
3,703	6,298
3,704	6,297
3,705	6,296
3,706	6,295

Hour	COUNTDOWN
3,707	6,294
3,708	6,293
3,709	6,292
3,710	6,291
3,711	6,290
3,712	6,289
3,713	6,288
3,714	6,287
3,715	6,286
3,716	6,285
3,717	6,284
3,718	6,283
3,719	6,282
3,720	6,281
3,721	6,280
3,722	6,279
3,723	6,278

Hour	COUNTDOWN
3,724	6,277
3,725	6,276
3,726	6,275
3,727	6,274
3,728	6,273
3,729	6,272
3,730	6,271
3,731	6,270
3,732	6,269
3,733	6,268
3,734	6,267
3,735	6,266
3,736	6,265
3,737	6,264
3,738	6,263
3,739	6,262
3,740	6,261

Hour	COUNTDOWN
3,741	6,260
3,742	6,259
3,743	6,258
3,744	6,257
3,745	6,256
3,746	6,255
3,747	6,254
3,748	6,253
3,749	6,252
3,750	6,251
3,751	6,250
3,752	6,249
3,753	6,248
3,754	6,247
3,755	6,246
3,756	6,245
3,757	6,244

Hour	COUNTDOWN
3,758	6,243
3,759	6,242
3,760	6,241
3,761	6,240
3,762	6,239
3,763	6,238
3,764	6,237
3,765	6,236
3,766	6,235
3,767	6,234
3,768	6,233
3,769	6,232
3,770	6,231
3,771	6,230
3,772	6,229
3,773	6,228
3,774	6,227

Hour	COUNTDOWN
3,775	6,226
3,776	6,225
3,777	6,224
3,778	6,223
3,779	6,222
3,780	6,221
3,781	6,220
3,782	6,219
3,783	6,218
3,784	6,217
3,785	6,216
3,786	6,215
3,787	6,214
3,788	6,213
3,789	6,212
3,790	6,211
3,791	6,210

Hour	COUNTDOWN
3,792	6,209
3,793	6,208
3,794	6,207
3,795	6,206
3,796	6,205
3,797	6,204
3,798	6,203
3,799	6,202
3,800	6,201
3,801	6,200
3,802	6,199
3,803	6,198
3,804	6,197
3,805	6,196
3,806	6,195
3,807	6,194
3,808	6,193

Hour	COUNTDOWN
3,809	6,192
3,810	6,191
3,811	6,190
3,812	6,189
3,813	6,188
3,814	6,187
3,815	6,186
3,816	6,185
3,817	6,184
3,818	6,183
3,819	6,182
3,820	6,181
3,821	6,180
3,822	6,179
3,823	6,178
3,824	6,177
3,825	6,176

Hour	COUNTDOWN
3,826	6,175
3,827	6,174
3,828	6,173
3,829	6,172
3,830	6,171
3,831	6,170
3,832	6,169
3,833	6,168
3,834	6,167
3,835	6,166
3,836	6,165
3,837	6,164
3,838	6,163
3,839	6,162
3,840	6,161
3,841	6,160
3,842	6,159

Hour	COUNTDOWN
3,843	6,158
3,844	6,157
3,845	6,156
3,846	6,155
3,847	6,154
3,848	6,153
3,849	6,152
3,850	6,151
3,851	6,150
3,852	6,149
3,853	6,148
3,854	6,147
3,855	6,146
3,856	6,145
3,857	6,144
3,858	6,143
3,859	6,142

Hour	COUNTDOWN
3,860	6,141
3,861	6,140
3,862	6,139
3,863	6,138
3,864	6,137
3,865	6,136
3,866	6,135
3,867	6,134
3,868	6,133
3,869	6,132
3,870	6,131
3,871	6,130
3,872	6,129
3,873	6,128
3,874	6,127
3,875	6,126
3,876	6,125

Hour	COUNTDOWN
3,877	6,124
3,878	6,123
3,879	6,122
3,880	6,121
3,881	6,120
3,882	6,119
3,883	6,118
3,884	6,117
3,885	6,116
3,886	6,115
3,887	6,114
3,888	6,113
3,889	6,112
3,890	6,111
3,891	6,110
3,892	6,109
3,893	6,108

Hour	COUNTDOWN
3,894	6,107
3,895	6,106
3,896	6,105
3,897	6,104
3,898	6,103
3,899	6,102
3,900	6,101
3,901	6,100
3,902	6,099
3,903	6,098
3,904	6,097
3,905	6,096
3,906	6,095
3,907	6,094
3,908	6,093
3,909	6,092
3,910	6,091

Hour	COUNTDOWN
3,911	6,090
3,912	6,089
3,913	6,088
3,914	6,087
3,915	6,086
3,916	6,085
3,917	6,084
3,918	6,083
3,919	6,082
3,920	6,081
3,921	6,080
3,922	6,079
3,923	6,078
3,924	6,077
3,925	6,076
3,926	6,075
3,927	6,074

Hour	COUNTDOWN
3,928	6,073
3,929	6,072
3,930	6,071
3,931	6,070
3,932	6,069
3,933	6,068
3,934	6,067
3,935	6,066
3,936	6,065
3,937	6,064
3,938	6,063
3,939	6,062
3,940	6,061
3,941	6,060
3,942	6,059
3,943	6,058
3,944	6,057

Hour	COUNTDOWN
3,945	6,056
3,946	6,055
3,947	6,054
3,948	6,053
3,949	6,052
3,950	6,051
3,951	6,050
3,952	6,049
3,953	6,048
3,954	6,047
3,955	6,046
3,956	6,045
3,957	6,044
3,958	6,043
3,959	6,042
3,960	6,041
3,961	6,040

Hour	COUNTDOWN
3,962	6,039
3,963	6,038
3,964	6,037
3,965	6,036
3,966	6,035
3,967	6,034
3,968	6,033
3,969	6,032
3,970	6,031
3,971	6,030
3,972	6,029
3,973	6,028
3,974	6,027
3,975	6,026
3,976	6,025
3,977	6,024
3,978	6,023

Hour	COUNTDOWN
3,979	6,022
3,980	6,021
3,981	6,020
3,982	6,019
3,983	6,018
3,984	6,017
3,985	6,016
3,986	6,015
3,987	6,014
3,988	6,013
3,989	6,012
3,990	6,011
3,991	6,010
3,992	6,009
3,993	6,008
3,994	6,007
3,995	6,006

Hour	COUNTDOWN
3,996	6,005
3,997	6,004
3,998	6,003
3,999	6,002
4,000	6,001
4,001	6,000
4,002	5,999
4,003	5,998
4,004	5,997
4,005	5,996
4,006	5,995
4,007	5,994
4,008	5,993
4,009	5,992
4,010	5,991
4,011	5,990
4,012	5,989

Hour	COUNTDOWN
4,013	5,988
4,014	5,987
4,015	5,986
4,016	5,985
4,017	5,984
4,018	5,983
4,019	5,982
4,020	5,981
4,021	5,980
4,022	5,979
4,023	5,978
4,024	5,977
4,025	5,976
4,026	5,975
4,027	5,974
4,028	5,973
4,029	5,972

Hour	COUNTDOWN
4,030	5,971
4,031	5,970
4,032	5,969
4,033	5,968
4,034	5,967
4,035	5,966
4,036	5,965
4,037	5,964
4,038	5,963
4,039	5,962
4,040	5,961
4,041	5,960
4,042	5,959
4,043	5,958
4,044	5,957
4,045	5,956
4,046	5,955

Hour	COUNTDOWN
4,047	5,954
4,048	5,953
4,049	5,952
4,050	5,951
4,051	5,950
4,052	5,949
4,053	5,948
4,054	5,947
4,055	5,946
4,056	5,945
4,057	5,944
4,058	5,943
4,059	5,942
4,060	5,941
4,061	5,940
4,062	5,939
4,063	5,938

Hour	COUNTDOWN
4,064	5,937
4,065	5,936
4,066	5,935
4,067	5,934
4,068	5,933
4,069	5,932
4,070	5,931
4,071	5,930
4,072	5,929
4,073	5,928
4,074	5,927
4,075	5,926
4,076	5,925
4,077	5,924
4,078	5,923
4,079	5,922
4,080	5,921

Hour	COUNTDOWN
4,081	5,920
4,082	5,919
4,083	5,918
4,084	5,917
4,085	5,916
4,086	5,915
4,087	5,914
4,088	5,913
4,089	5,912
4,090	5,911
4,091	5,910
4,092	5,909
4,093	5,908
4,094	5,907
4,095	5,906
4,096	5,905
4,097	5,904

Hour	COUNTDOWN
4,098	5,903
4,099	5,902
4,100	5,901
4,101	5,900
4,102	5,899
4,103	5,898
4,104	5,897
4,105	5,896
4,106	5,895
4,107	5,894
4,108	5,893
4,109	5,892
4,110	5,891
4,111	5,890
4,112	5,889
4,113	5,888
4,114	5,887

Hour	COUNTDOWN
4,115	5,886
4,116	5,885
4,117	5,884
4,118	5,883
4,119	5,882
4,120	5,881
4,121	5,880
4,122	5,879
4,123	5,878
4,124	5,877
4,125	5,876
4,126	5,875
4,127	5,874
4,128	5,873
4,129	5,872
4,130	5,871
4,131	5,870

Hour	COUNTDOWN
4,132	5,869
4,133	5,868
4,134	5,867
4,135	5,866
4,136	5,865
4,137	5,864
4,138	5,863
4,139	5,862
4,140	5,861
4,141	5,860
4,142	5,859
4,143	5,858
4,144	5,857
4,145	5,856
4,146	5,855
4,147	5,854
4,148	5,853

Hour	COUNTDOWN
4,149	5,852
4,150	5,851
4,151	5,850
4,152	5,849
4,153	5,848
4,154	5,847
4,155	5,846
4,156	5,845
4,157	5,844
4,158	5,843
4,159	5,842
4,160	5,841
4,161	5,840
4,162	5,839
4,163	5,838
4,164	5,837
4,165	5,836

Hour	COUNTDOWN
4,166	5,835
4,167	5,834
4,168	5,833
4,169	5,832
4,170	5,831
4,171	5,830
4,172	5,829
4,173	5,828
4,174	5,827
4,175	5,826
4,176	5,825
4,177	5,824
4,178	5,823
4,179	5,822
4,180	5,821
4,181	5,820
4,182	5,819

Hour	COUNTDOWN
4,183	5,818
4,184	5,817
4,185	5,816
4,186	5,815
4,187	5,814
4,188	5,813
4,189	5,812
4,190	5,811
4,191	5,810
4,192	5,809
4,193	5,808
4,194	5,807
4,195	5,806
4,196	5,805
4,197	5,804
4,198	5,803
4,199	5,802

Hour	COUNTDOWN
4,200	5,801
4,201	5,800
4,202	5,799
4,203	5,798
4,204	5,797
4,205	5,796
4,206	5,795
4,207	5,794
4,208	5,793
4,209	5,792
4,210	5,791
4,211	5,790
4,212	5,789
4,213	5,788
4,214	5,787
4,215	5,786
4,216	5,785

Hour	COUNTDOWN
4,217	5,784
4,218	5,783
4,219	5,782
4,220	5,781
4,221	5,780
4,222	5,779
4,223	5,778
4,224	5,777
4,225	5,776
4,226	5,775
4,227	5,774
4,228	5,773
4,229	5,772
4,230	5,771
4,231	5,770
4,232	5,769
4,233	5,768

Hour	COUNTDOWN
4,234	5,767
4,235	5,766
4,236	5,765
4,237	5,764
4,238	5,763
4,239	5,762
4,240	5,761
4,241	5,760
4,242	5,759
4,243	5,758
4,244	5,757
4,245	5,756
4,246	5,755
4,247	5,754
4,248	5,753
4,249	5,752
4,250	5,751

Hour	COUNTDOWN
4,251	5,750
4,252	5,749
4,253	5,748
4,254	5,747
4,255	5,746
4,256	5,745
4,257	5,744
4,258	5,743
4,259	5,742
4,260	5,741
4,261	5,740
4,262	5,739
4,263	5,738
4,264	5,737
4,265	5,736
4,266	5,735
4,267	5,734

Hour	COUNTDOWN
4,268	5,733
4,269	5,732
4,270	5,731
4,271	5,730
4,272	5,729
4,273	5,728
4,274	5,727
4,275	5,726
4,276	5,725
4,277	5,724
4,278	5,723
4,279	5,722
4,280	5,721
4,281	5,720
4,282	5,719
4,283	5,718
4,284	5,717

Hour	COUNTDOWN
4,285	5,716
4,286	5,715
4,287	5,714
4,288	5,713
4,289	5,712
4,290	5,711
4,291	5,710
4,292	5,709
4,293	5,708
4,294	5,707
4,295	5,706
4,296	5,705
4,297	5,704
4,298	5,703
4,299	5,702
4,300	5,701
4,301	5,700

Hour	COUNTDOWN
4,302	5,699
4,303	5,698
4,304	5,697
4,305	5,696
4,306	5,695
4,307	5,694
4,308	5,693
4,309	5,692
4,310	5,691
4,311	5,690
4,312	5,689
4,313	5,688
4,314	5,687
4,315	5,686
4,316	5,685
4,317	5,684
4,318	5,683

Hour	COUNTDOWN
4,319	5,682
4,320	5,681
4,321	5,680
4,322	5,679
4,323	5,678
4,324	5,677
4,325	5,676
4,326	5,675
4,327	5,674
4,328	5,673
4,329	5,672
4,330	5,671
4,331	5,670
4,332	5,669
4,333	5,668
4,334	5,667
4,335	5,666

Hour	COUNTDOWN
4,336	5,665
4,337	5,664
4,338	5,663
4,339	5,662
4,340	5,661
4,341	5,660
4,342	5,659
4,343	5,658
4,344	5,657
4,345	5,656
4,346	5,655
4,347	5,654
4,348	5,653
4,349	5,652
4,350	5,651
4,351	5,650
4,352	5,649

Hour	COUNTDOWN
4,353	5,648
4,354	5,647
4,355	5,646
4,356	5,645
4,357	5,644
4,358	5,643
4,359	5,642
4,360	5,641
4,361	5,640
4,362	5,639
4,363	5,638
4,364	5,637
4,365	5,636
4,366	5,635
4,367	5,634
4,368	5,633
4,369	5,632

Hour	COUNTDOWN
4,370	5,631
4,371	5,630
4,372	5,629
4,373	5,628
4,374	5,627
4,375	5,626
4,376	5,625
4,377	5,624
4,378	5,623
4,379	5,622
4,380	5,621
4,381	5,620
4,382	5,619
4,383	5,618
4,384	5,617
4,385	5,616
4,386	5,615

Hour	COUNTDOWN
4,387	5,614
4,388	5,613
4,389	5,612
4,390	5,611
4,391	5,610
4,392	5,609
4,393	5,608
4,394	5,607
4,395	5,606
4,396	5,605
4,397	5,604
4,398	5,603
4,399	5,602
4,400	5,601
4,401	5,600
4,402	5,599
4,403	5,598

Hour	COUNTDOWN
4,404	5,597
4,405	5,596
4,406	5,595
4,407	5,594
4,408	5,593
4,409	5,592
4,410	5,591
4,411	5,590
4,412	5,589
4,413	5,588
4,414	5,587
4,415	5,586
4,416	5,585
4,417	5,584
4,418	5,583
4,419	5,582
4,420	5,581

Hour	COUNTDOWN
4,421	5,580
4,422	5,579
4,423	5,578
4,424	5,577
4,425	5,576
4,426	5,575
4,427	5,574
4,428	5,573
4,429	5,572
4,430	5,571
4,431	5,570
4,432	5,569
4,433	5,568
4,434	5,567
4,435	5,566
4,436	5,565
4,437	5,564

Hour	COUNTDOWN
4,438	5,563
4,439	5,562
4,440	5,561
4,441	5,560
4,442	5,559
4,443	5,558
4,444	5,557
4,445	5,556
4,446	5,555
4,447	5,554
4,448	5,553
4,449	5,552
4,450	5,551
4,451	5,550
4,452	5,549
4,453	5,548
4,454	5,547

Hour	COUNTDOWN
4,455	5,546
4,456	5,545
4,457	5,544
4,458	5,543
4,459	5,542
4,460	5,541
4,461	5,540
4,462	5,539
4,463	5,538
4,464	5,537
4,465	5,536
4,466	5,535
4,467	5,534
4,468	5,533
4,469	5,532
4,470	5,531
4,471	5,530

Hour	COUNTDOWN
4,472	5,529
4,473	5,528
4,474	5,527
4,475	5,526
4,476	5,525
4,477	5,524
4,478	5,523
4,479	5,522
4,480	5,521
4,481	5,520
4,482	5,519
4,483	5,518
4,484	5,517
4,485	5,516
4,486	5,515
4,487	5,514
4,488	5,513

Hour	COUNTDOWN
4,489	5,512
4,490	5,511
4,491	5,510
4,492	5,509
4,493	5,508
4,494	5,507
4,495	5,506
4,496	5,505
4,497	5,504
4,498	5,503
4,499	5,502
4,500	5,501
4,501	5,500
4,502	5,499
4,503	5,498
4,504	5,497
4,505	5,496

Hour	COUNTDOWN
4,506	5,495
4,507	5,494
4,508	5,493
4,509	5,492
4,510	5,491
4,511	5,490
4,512	5,489
4,513	5,488
4,514	5,487
4,515	5,486
4,516	5,485
4,517	5,484
4,518	5,483
4,519	5,482
4,520	5,481
4,521	5,480
4,522	5,479

Hour	COUNTDOWN
4,523	5,478
4,524	5,477
4,525	5,476
4,526	5,475
4,527	5,474
4,528	5,473
4,529	5,472
4,530	5,471
4,531	5,470
4,532	5,469
4,533	5,468
4,534	5,467
4,535	5,466
4,536	5,465
4,537	5,464
4,538	5,463
4,539	5,462

Hour	COUNTDOWN
4,540	5,461
4,541	5,460
4,542	5,459
4,543	5,458
4,544	5,457
4,545	5,456
4,546	5,455
4,547	5,454
4,548	5,453
4,549	5,452
4,550	5,451
4,551	5,450
4,552	5,449
4,553	5,448
4,554	5,447
4,555	5,446
4,556	5,445

Hour	COUNTDOWN
4,557	5,444
4,558	5,443
4,559	5,442
4,560	5,441
4,561	5,440
4,562	5,439
4,563	5,438
4,564	5,437
4,565	5,436
4,566	5,435
4,567	5,434
4,568	5,433
4,569	5,432
4,570	5,431
4,571	5,430
4,572	5,429
4,573	5,428

Hour	COUNTDOWN
4,574	5,427
4,575	5,426
4,576	5,425
4,577	5,424
4,578	5,423
4,579	5,422
4,580	5,421
4,581	5,420
4,582	5,419
4,583	5,418
4,584	5,417
4,585	5,416
4,586	5,415
4,587	5,414
4,588	5,413
4,589	5,412
4,590	5,411

Hour	COUNTDOWN
4,591	5,410
4,592	5,409
4,593	5,408
4,594	5,407
4,595	5,406
4,596	5,405
4,597	5,404
4,598	5,403
4,599	5,402
4,600	5,401
4,601	5,400
4,602	5,399
4,603	5,398
4,604	5,397
4,605	5,396
4,606	5,395
4,607	5,394

Hour	COUNTDOWN
4,608	5,393
4,609	5,392
4,610	5,391
4,611	5,390
4,612	5,389
4,613	5,388
4,614	5,387
4,615	5,386
4,616	5,385
4,617	5,384
4,618	5,383
4,619	5,382
4,620	5,381
4,621	5,380
4,622	5,379
4,623	5,378
4,624	5,377

Hour	COUNTDOWN
4,625	5,376
4,626	5,375
4,627	5,374
4,628	5,373
4,629	5,372
4,630	5,371
4,631	5,370
4,632	5,369
4,633	5,368
4,634	5,367
4,635	5,366
4,636	5,365
4,637	5,364
4,638	5,363
4,639	5,362
4,640	5,361
4,641	5,360

Hour	COUNTDOWN
4,642	5,359
4,643	5,358
4,644	5,357
4,645	5,356
4,646	5,355
4,647	5,354
4,648	5,353
4,649	5,352
4,650	5,351
4,651	5,350
4,652	5,349
4,653	5,348
4,654	5,347
4,655	5,346
4,656	5,345
4,657	5,344
4,658	5,343

Hour	COUNTDOWN
4,659	5,342
4,660	5,341
4,661	5,340
4,662	5,339
4,663	5,338
4,664	5,337
4,665	5,336
4,666	5,335
4,667	5,334
4,668	5,333
4,669	5,332
4,670	5,331
4,671	5,330
4,672	5,329
4,673	5,328
4,674	5,327
4,675	5,326

Hour	COUNTDOWN
4,676	5,325
4,677	5,324
4,678	5,323
4,679	5,322
4,680	5,321
4,681	5,320
4,682	5,319
4,683	5,318
4,684	5,317
4,685	5,316
4,686	5,315
4,687	5,314
4,688	5,313
4,689	5,312
4,690	5,311
4,691	5,310
4,692	5,309

Hour	COUNTDOWN
4,693	5,308
4,694	5,307
4,695	5,306
4,696	5,305
4,697	5,304
4,698	5,303
4,699	5,302
4,700	5,301
4,701	5,300
4,702	5,299
4,703	5,298
4,704	5,297
4,705	5,296
4,706	5,295
4,707	5,294
4,708	5,293
4,709	5,292

Hour	COUNTDOWN
4,710	5,291
4,711	5,290
4,712	5,289
4,713	5,288
4,714	5,287
4,715	5,286
4,716	5,285
4,717	5,284
4,718	5,283
4,719	5,282
4,720	5,281
4,721	5,280
4,722	5,279
4,723	5,278
4,724	5,277
4,725	5,276
4,726	5,275

Hour	COUNTDOWN
4,727	5,274
4,728	5,273
4,729	5,272
4,730	5,271
4,731	5,270
4,732	5,269
4,733	5,268
4,734	5,267
4,735	5,266
4,736	5,265
4,737	5,264
4,738	5,263
4,739	5,262
4,740	5,261
4,741	5,260
4,742	5,259
4,743	5,258

Hour	COUNTDOWN
4,744	5,257
4,745	5,256
4,746	5,255
4,747	5,254
4,748	5,253
4,749	5,252
4,750	5,251
4,751	5,250
4,752	5,249
4,753	5,248
4,754	5,247
4,755	5,246
4,756	5,245
4,757	5,244
4,758	5,243
4,759	5,242
4,760	5,241

Hour	COUNTDOWN
4,761	5,240
4,762	5,239
4,763	5,238
4,764	5,237
4,765	5,236
4,766	5,235
4,767	5,234
4,768	5,233
4,769	5,232
4,770	5,231
4,771	5,230
4,772	5,229
4,773	5,228
4,774	5,227
4,775	5,226
4,776	5,225
4,777	5,224

Hour	COUNTDOWN
4,778	5,223
4,779	5,222
4,780	5,221
4,781	5,220
4,782	5,219
4,783	5,218
4,784	5,217
4,785	5,216
4,786	5,215
4,787	5,214
4,788	5,213
4,789	5,212
4,790	5,211
4,791	5,210
4,792	5,209
4,793	5,208
4,794	5,207

Hour	COUNTDOWN
4,795	5,206
4,796	5,205
4,797	5,204
4,798	5,203
4,799	5,202
4,800	5,201
4,801	5,200
4,802	5,199
4,803	5,198
4,804	5,197
4,805	5,196
4,806	5,195
4,807	5,194
4,808	5,193
4,809	5,192
4,810	5,191
4,811	5,190

Hour	COUNTDOWN
4,812	5,189
4,813	5,188
4,814	5,187
4,815	5,186
4,816	5,185
4,817	5,184
4,818	5,183
4,819	5,182
4,820	5,181
4,821	5,180
4,822	5,179
4,823	5,178
4,824	5,177
4,825	5,176
4,826	5,175
4,827	5,174
4,828	5,173

Hour	COUNTDOWN
4,829	5,172
4,830	5,171
4,831	5,170
4,832	5,169
4,833	5,168
4,834	5,167
4,835	5,166
4,836	5,165
4,837	5,164
4,838	5,163
4,839	5,162
4,840	5,161
4,841	5,160
4,842	5,159
4,843	5,158
4,844	5,157
4,845	5,156

Hour	COUNTDOWN
4,846	5,155
4,847	5,154
4,848	5,153
4,849	5,152
4,850	5,151
4,851	5,150
4,852	5,149
4,853	5,148
4,854	5,147
4,855	5,146
4,856	5,145
4,857	5,144
4,858	5,143
4,859	5,142
4,860	5,141
4,861	5,140
4,862	5,139

Hour	COUNTDOWN
4,863	5,138
4,864	5,137
4,865	5,136
4,866	5,135
4,867	5,134
4,868	5,133
4,869	5,132
4,870	5,131
4,871	5,130
4,872	5,129
4,873	5,128
4,874	5,127
4,875	5,126
4,876	5,125
4,877	5,124
4,878	5,123
4,879	5,122

Hour	COUNTDOWN
4,880	5,121
4,881	5,120
4,882	5,119
4,883	5,118
4,884	5,117
4,885	5,116
4,886	5,115
4,887	5,114
4,888	5,113
4,889	5,112
4,890	5,111
4,891	5,110
4,892	5,109
4,893	5,108
4,894	5,107
4,895	5,106
4,896	5,105

Hour	COUNTDOWN
4,897	5,104
4,898	5,103
4,899	5,102
4,900	5,101
4,901	5,100
4,902	5,099
4,903	5,098
4,904	5,097
4,905	5,096
4,906	5,095
4,907	5,094
4,908	5,093
4,909	5,092
4,910	5,091
4,911	5,090
4,912	5,089
4,913	5,088

Hour	COUNTDOWN
4,914	5,087
4,915	5,086
4,916	5,085
4,917	5,084
4,918	5,083
4,919	5,082
4,920	5,081
4,921	5,080
4,922	5,079
4,923	5,078
4,924	5,077
4,925	5,076
4,926	5,075
4,927	5,074
4,928	5,073
4,929	5,072
4,930	5,071

Hour	COUNTDOWN
4,931	5,070
4,932	5,069
4,933	5,068
4,934	5,067
4,935	5,066
4,936	5,065
4,937	5,064
4,938	5,063
4,939	5,062
4,940	5,061
4,941	5,060
4,942	5,059
4,943	5,058
4,944	5,057
4,945	5,056
4,946	5,055
4,947	5,054

Hour	COUNTDOWN
4,948	5,053
4,949	5,052
4,950	5,051
4,951	5,050
4,952	5,049
4,953	5,048
4,954	5,047
4,955	5,046
4,956	5,045
4,957	5,044
4,958	5,043
4,959	5,042
4,960	5,041
4,961	5,040
4,962	5,039
4,963	5,038
4,964	5,037

Hour	COUNTDOWN
4,965	5,036
4,966	5,035
4,967	5,034
4,968	5,033
4,969	5,032
4,970	5,031
4,971	5,030
4,972	5,029
4,973	5,028
4,974	5,027
4,975	5,026
4,976	5,025
4,977	5,024
4,978	5,023
4,979	5,022
4,980	5,021
4,981	5,020

Hour	COUNTDOWN
4,982	5,019
4,983	5,018
4,984	5,017
4,985	5,016
4,986	5,015
4,987	5,014
4,988	5,013
4,989	5,012
4,990	5,011
4,991	5,010
4,992	5,009
4,993	5,008
4,994	5,007
4,995	5,006
4,996	5,005
4,997	5,004
4,998	5,003

Hour	COUNTDOWN
4,999	5,002
5,000	5,001
5,001	5,000
5,002	4,999
5,003	4,998
5,004	4,997
5,005	4,996
5,006	4,995
5,007	4,994
5,008	4,993
5,009	4,992
5,010	4,991
5,011	4,990
5,012	4,989
5,013	4,988
5,014	4,987
5,015	4,986

Hour	COUNTDOWN
5,016	4,985
5,017	4,984
5,018	4,983
5,019	4,982
5,020	4,981
5,021	4,980
5,022	4,979
5,023	4,978
5,024	4,977
5,025	4,976
5,026	4,975
5,027	4,974
5,028	4,973
5,029	4,972
5,030	4,971
5,031	4,970
5,032	4,969

Hour	COUNTDOWN
5,033	4,968
5,034	4,967
5,035	4,966
5,036	4,965
5,037	4,964
5,038	4,963
5,039	4,962
5,040	4,961
5,041	4,960
5,042	4,959
5,043	4,958
5,044	4,957
5,045	4,956
5,046	4,955
5,047	4,954
5,048	4,953
5,049	4,952

Hour	COUNTDOWN
5,050	4,951
5,051	4,950
5,052	4,949
5,053	4,948
5,054	4,947
5,055	4,946
5,056	4,945
5,057	4,944
5,058	4,943
5,059	4,942
5,060	4,941
5,061	4,940
5,062	4,939
5,063	4,938
5,064	4,937
5,065	4,936
5,066	4,935

Hour	COUNTDOWN
5,067	4,934
5,068	4,933
5,069	4,932
5,070	4,931
5,071	4,930
5,072	4,929
5,073	4,928
5,074	4,927
5,075	4,926
5,076	4,925
5,077	4,924
5,078	4,923
5,079	4,922
5,080	4,921
5,081	4,920
5,082	4,919
5,083	4,918

Hour	COUNTDOWN
5,084	4,917
5,085	4,916
5,086	4,915
5,087	4,914
5,088	4,913
5,089	4,912
5,090	4,911
5,091	4,910
5,092	4,909
5,093	4,908
5,094	4,907
5,095	4,906
5,096	4,905
5,097	4,904
5,098	4,903
5,099	4,902
5,100	4,901

Hour	COUNTDOWN
5,101	4,900
5,102	4,899
5,103	4,898
5,104	4,897
5,105	4,896
5,106	4,895
5,107	4,894
5,108	4,893
5,109	4,892
5,110	4,891
5,111	4,890
5,112	4,889
5,113	4,888
5,114	4,887
5,115	4,886
5,116	4,885
5,117	4,884

Hour	COUNTDOWN
5,118	4,883
5,119	4,882
5,120	4,881
5,121	4,880
5,122	4,879
5,123	4,878
5,124	4,877
5,125	4,876
5,126	4,875
5,127	4,874
5,128	4,873
5,129	4,872
5,130	4,871
5,131	4,870
5,132	4,869
5,133	4,868
5,134	4,867

Hour	COUNTDOWN
5,135	4,866
5,136	4,865
5,137	4,864
5,138	4,863
5,139	4,862
5,140	4,861
5,141	4,860
5,142	4,859
5,143	4,858
5,144	4,857
5,145	4,856
5,146	4,855
5,147	4,854
5,148	4,853
5,149	4,852
5,150	4,851
5,151	4,850

Hour	COUNTDOWN
5,152	4,849
5,153	4,848
5,154	4,847
5,155	4,846
5,156	4,845
5,157	4,844
5,158	4,843
5,159	4,842
5,160	4,841
5,161	4,840
5,162	4,839
5,163	4,838
5,164	4,837
5,165	4,836
5,166	4,835
5,167	4,834
5,168	4,833

Hour	COUNTDOWN
5,169	4,832
5,170	4,831
5,171	4,830
5,172	4,829
5,173	4,828
5,174	4,827
5,175	4,826
5,176	4,825
5,177	4,824
5,178	4,823
5,179	4,822
5,180	4,821
5,181	4,820
5,182	4,819
5,183	4,818
5,184	4,817
5,185	4,816

Hour	COUNTDOWN
5,186	4,815
5,187	4,814
5,188	4,813
5,189	4,812
5,190	4,811
5,191	4,810
5,192	4,809
5,193	4,808
5,194	4,807
5,195	4,806
5,196	4,805
5,197	4,804
5,198	4,803
5,199	4,802
5,200	4,801
5,201	4,800
5,202	4,799

Hour	COUNTDOWN
5,203	4,798
5,204	4,797
5,205	4,796
5,206	4,795
5,207	4,794
5,208	4,793
5,209	4,792
5,210	4,791
5,211	4,790
5,212	4,789
5,213	4,788
5,214	4,787
5,215	4,786
5,216	4,785
5,217	4,784
5,218	4,783
5,219	4,782

Hour	COUNTDOWN
5,220	4,781
5,221	4,780
5,222	4,779
5,223	4,778
5,224	4,777
5,225	4,776
5,226	4,775
5,227	4,774
5,228	4,773
5,229	4,772
5,230	4,771
5,231	4,770
5,232	4,769
5,233	4,768
5,234	4,767
5,235	4,766
5,236	4,765

Hour	COUNTDOWN
5,237	4,764
5,238	4,763
5,239	4,762
5,240	4,761
5,241	4,760
5,242	4,759
5,243	4,758
5,244	4,757
5,245	4,756
5,246	4,755
5,247	4,754
5,248	4,753
5,249	4,752
5,250	4,751
5,251	4,750
5,252	4,749
5,253	4,748

Hour	COUNTDOWN
5,254	4,747
5,255	4,746
5,256	4,745
5,257	4,744
5,258	4,743
5,259	4,742
5,260	4,741
5,261	4,740
5,262	4,739
5,263	4,738
5,264	4,737
5,265	4,736
5,266	4,735
5,267	4,734
5,268	4,733
5,269	4,732
5,270	4,731

Hour	COUNTDOWN
5,271	4,730
5,272	4,729
5,273	4,728
5,274	4,727
5,275	4,726
5,276	4,725
5,277	4,724
5,278	4,723
5,279	4,722
5,280	4,721
5,281	4,720
5,282	4,719
5,283	4,718
5,284	4,717
5,285	4,716
5,286	4,715
5,287	4,714

Hour	COUNTDOWN
5,288	4,713
5,289	4,712
5,290	4,711
5,291	4,710
5,292	4,709
5,293	4,708
5,294	4,707
5,295	4,706
5,296	4,705
5,297	4,704
5,298	4,703
5,299	4,702
5,300	4,701
5,301	4,700
5,302	4,699
5,303	4,698
5,304	4,697

Hour	COUNTDOWN
5,305	4,696
5,306	4,695
5,307	4,694
5,308	4,693
5,309	4,692
5,310	4,691
5,311	4,690
5,312	4,689
5,313	4,688
5,314	4,687
5,315	4,686
5,316	4,685
5,317	4,684
5,318	4,683
5,319	4,682
5,320	4,681
5,321	4,680

Hour	COUNTDOWN
5,322	4,679
5,323	4,678
5,324	4,677
5,325	4,676
5,326	4,675
5,327	4,674
5,328	4,673
5,329	4,672
5,330	4,671
5,331	4,670
5,332	4,669
5,333	4,668
5,334	4,667
5,335	4,666
5,336	4,665
5,337	4,664
5,338	4,663

Hour	COUNTDOWN
5,339	4,662
5,340	4,661
5,341	4,660
5,342	4,659
5,343	4,658
5,344	4,657
5,345	4,656
5,346	4,655
5,347	4,654
5,348	4,653
5,349	4,652
5,350	4,651
5,351	4,650
5,352	4,649
5,353	4,648
5,354	4,647
5,355	4,646

Hour	COUNTDOWN
5,356	4,645
5,357	4,644
5,358	4,643
5,359	4,642
5,360	4,641
5,361	4,640
5,362	4,639
5,363	4,638
5,364	4,637
5,365	4,636
5,366	4,635
5,367	4,634
5,368	4,633
5,369	4,632
5,370	4,631
5,371	4,630
5,372	4,629

Hour	COUNTDOWN
5,373	4,628
5,374	4,627
5,375	4,626
5,376	4,625
5,377	4,624
5,378	4,623
5,379	4,622
5,380	4,621
5,381	4,620
5,382	4,619
5,383	4,618
5,384	4,617
5,385	4,616
5,386	4,615
5,387	4,614
5,388	4,613
5,389	4,612

Hour	COUNTDOWN
5,390	4,611
5,391	4,610
5,392	4,609
5,393	4,608
5,394	4,607
5,395	4,606
5,396	4,605
5,397	4,604
5,398	4,603
5,399	4,602
5,400	4,601
5,401	4,600
5,402	4,599
5,403	4,598
5,404	4,597
5,405	4,596
5,406	4,595

Hour	COUNTDOWN
5,407	4,594
5,408	4,593
5,409	4,592
5,410	4,591
5,411	4,590
5,412	4,589
5,413	4,588
5,414	4,587
5,415	4,586
5,416	4,585
5,417	4,584
5,418	4,583
5,419	4,582
5,420	4,581
5,421	4,580
5,422	4,579
5,423	4,578

Hour	COUNTDOWN
5,424	4,577
5,425	4,576
5,426	4,575
5,427	4,574
5,428	4,573
5,429	4,572
5,430	4,571
5,431	4,570
5,432	4,569
5,433	4,568
5,434	4,567
5,435	4,566
5,436	4,565
5,437	4,564
5,438	4,563
5,439	4,562
5,440	4,561

Hour	COUNTDOWN
5,441	4,560
5,442	4,559
5,443	4,558
5,444	4,557
5,445	4,556
5,446	4,555
5,447	4,554
5,448	4,553
5,449	4,552
5,450	4,551
5,451	4,550
5,452	4,549
5,453	4,548
5,454	4,547
5,455	4,546
5,456	4,545
5,457	4,544

Hour	COUNTDOWN
5,458	4,543
5,459	4,542
5,460	4,541
5,461	4,540
5,462	4,539
5,463	4,538
5,464	4,537
5,465	4,536
5,466	4,535
5,467	4,534
5,468	4,533
5,469	4,532
5,470	4,531
5,471	4,530
5,472	4,529
5,473	4,528
5,474	4,527

Hour	COUNTDOWN
5,475	4,526
5,476	4,525
5,477	4,524
5,478	4,523
5,479	4,522
5,480	4,521
5,481	4,520
5,482	4,519
5,483	4,518
5,484	4,517
5,485	4,516
5,486	4,515
5,487	4,514
5,488	4,513
5,489	4,512
5,490	4,511
5,491	4,510

Hour	COUNTDOWN
5,492	4,509
5,493	4,508
5,494	4,507
5,495	4,506
5,496	4,505
5,497	4,504
5,498	4,503
5,499	4,502
5,500	4,501
5,501	4,500
5,502	4,499
5,503	4,498
5,504	4,497
5,505	4,496
5,506	4,495
5,507	4,494
5,508	4,493

Hour	COUNTDOWN
5,509	4,492
5,510	4,491
5,511	4,490
5,512	4,489
5,513	4,488
5,514	4,487
5,515	4,486
5,516	4,485
5,517	4,484
5,518	4,483
5,519	4,482
5,520	4,481
5,521	4,480
5,522	4,479
5,523	4,478
5,524	4,477
5,525	4,476

Hour	COUNTDOWN
5,526	4,475
5,527	4,474
5,528	4,473
5,529	4,472
5,530	4,471
5,531	4,470
5,532	4,469
5,533	4,468
5,534	4,467
5,535	4,466
5,536	4,465
5,537	4,464
5,538	4,463
5,539	4,462
5,540	4,461
5,541	4,460
5,542	4,459

Hour	COUNTDOWN
5,543	4,458
5,544	4,457
5,545	4,456
5,546	4,455
5,547	4,454
5,548	4,453
5,549	4,452
5,550	4,451
5,551	4,450
5,552	4,449
5,553	4,448
5,554	4,447
5,555	4,446
5,556	4,445
5,557	4,444
5,558	4,443
5,559	4,442

Hour	COUNTDOWN
5,560	4,441
5,561	4,440
5,562	4,439
5,563	4,438
5,564	4,437
5,565	4,436
5,566	4,435
5,567	4,434
5,568	4,433
5,569	4,432
5,570	4,431
5,571	4,430
5,572	4,429
5,573	4,428
5,574	4,427
5,575	4,426
5,576	4,425

Hour	COUNTDOWN
5,577	4,424
5,578	4,423
5,579	4,422
5,580	4,421
5,581	4,420
5,582	4,419
5,583	4,418
5,584	4,417
5,585	4,416
5,586	4,415
5,587	4,414
5,588	4,413
5,589	4,412
5,590	4,411
5,591	4,410
5,592	4,409
5,593	4,408

Hour	COUNTDOWN
5,594	4,407
5,595	4,406
5,596	4,405
5,597	4,404
5,598	4,403
5,599	4,402
5,600	4,401
5,601	4,400
5,602	4,399
5,603	4,398
5,604	4,397
5,605	4,396
5,606	4,395
5,607	4,394
5,608	4,393
5,609	4,392
5,610	4,391

Hour	COUNTDOWN
5,611	4,390
5,612	4,389
5,613	4,388
5,614	4,387
5,615	4,386
5,616	4,385
5,617	4,384
5,618	4,383
5,619	4,382
5,620	4,381
5,621	4,380
5,622	4,379
5,623	4,378
5,624	4,377
5,625	4,376
5,626	4,375
5,627	4,374

Hour	COUNTDOWN
5,628	4,373
5,629	4,372
5,630	4,371
5,631	4,370
5,632	4,369
5,633	4,368
5,634	4,367
5,635	4,366
5,636	4,365
5,637	4,364
5,638	4,363
5,639	4,362
5,640	4,361
5,641	4,360
5,642	4,359
5,643	4,358
5,644	4,357

Hour	COUNTDOWN
5,645	4,356
5,646	4,355
5,647	4,354
5,648	4,353
5,649	4,352
5,650	4,351
5,651	4,350
5,652	4,349
5,653	4,348
5,654	4,347
5,655	4,346
5,656	4,345
5,657	4,344
5,658	4,343
5,659	4,342
5,660	4,341
5,661	4,340

Hour	COUNTDOWN
5,662	4,339
5,663	4,338
5,664	4,337
5,665	4,336
5,666	4,335
5,667	4,334
5,668	4,333
5,669	4,332
5,670	4,331
5,671	4,330
5,672	4,329
5,673	4,328
5,674	4,327
5,675	4,326
5,676	4,325
5,677	4,324
5,678	4,323

Hour	COUNTDOWN
5,679	4,322
5,680	4,321
5,681	4,320
5,682	4,319
5,683	4,318
5,684	4,317
5,685	4,316
5,686	4,315
5,687	4,314
5,688	4,313
5,689	4,312
5,690	4,311
5,691	4,310
5,692	4,309
5,693	4,308
5,694	4,307
5,695	4,306

Hour	COUNTDOWN
5,696	4,305
5,697	4,304
5,698	4,303
5,699	4,302
5,700	4,301
5,701	4,300
5,702	4,299
5,703	4,298
5,704	4,297
5,705	4,296
5,706	4,295
5,707	4,294
5,708	4,293
5,709	4,292
5,710	4,291
5,711	4,290
5,712	4,289

Hour	COUNTDOWN
5,713	4,288
5,714	4,287
5,715	4,286
5,716	4,285
5,717	4,284
5,718	4,283
5,719	4,282
5,720	4,281
5,721	4,280
5,722	4,279
5,723	4,278
5,724	4,277
5,725	4,276
5,726	4,275
5,727	4,274
5,728	4,273
5,729	4,272

Hour	COUNTDOWN
5,730	4,271
5,731	4,270
5,732	4,269
5,733	4,268
5,734	4,267
5,735	4,266
5,736	4,265
5,737	4,264
5,738	4,263
5,739	4,262
5,740	4,261
5,741	4,260
5,742	4,259
5,743	4,258
5,744	4,257
5,745	4,256
5,746	4,255

Hour	COUNTDOWN
5,747	4,254
5,748	4,253
5,749	4,252
5,750	4,251
5,751	4,250
5,752	4,249
5,753	4,248
5,754	4,247
5,755	4,246
5,756	4,245
5,757	4,244
5,758	4,243
5,759	4,242
5,760	4,241
5,761	4,240
5,762	4,239
5,763	4,238

Hour	COUNTDOWN
5,764	4,237
5,765	4,236
5,766	4,235
5,767	4,234
5,768	4,233
5,769	4,232
5,770	4,231
5,771	4,230
5,772	4,229
5,773	4,228
5,774	4,227
5,775	4,226
5,776	4,225
5,777	4,224
5,778	4,223
5,779	4,222
5,780	4,221

Hour	COUNTDOWN
5,781	4,220
5,782	4,219
5,783	4,218
5,784	4,217
5,785	4,216
5,786	4,215
5,787	4,214
5,788	4,213
5,789	4,212
5,790	4,211
5,791	4,210
5,792	4,209
5,793	4,208
5,794	4,207
5,795	4,206
5,796	4,205
5,797	4,204

Hour	COUNTDOWN
5,798	4,203
5,799	4,202
5,800	4,201
5,801	4,200
5,802	4,199
5,803	4,198
5,804	4,197
5,805	4,196
5,806	4,195
5,807	4,194
5,808	4,193
5,809	4,192
5,810	4,191
5,811	4,190
5,812	4,189
5,813	4,188
5,814	4,187

Hour	COUNTDOWN
5,815	4,186
5,816	4,185
5,817	4,184
5,818	4,183
5,819	4,182
5,820	4,181
5,821	4,180
5,822	4,179
5,823	4,178
5,824	4,177
5,825	4,176
5,826	4,175
5,827	4,174
5,828	4,173
5,829	4,172
5,830	4,171
5,831	4,170

Hour	COUNTDOWN
5,832	4,169
5,833	4,168
5,834	4,167
5,835	4,166
5,836	4,165
5,837	4,164
5,838	4,163
5,839	4,162
5,840	4,161
5,841	4,160
5,842	4,159
5,843	4,158
5,844	4,157
5,845	4,156
5,846	4,155
5,847	4,154
5,848	4,153

Hour	COUNTDOWN
5,849	4,152
5,850	4,151
5,851	4,150
5,852	4,149
5,853	4,148
5,854	4,147
5,855	4,146
5,856	4,145
5,857	4,144
5,858	4,143
5,859	4,142
5,860	4,141
5,861	4,140
5,862	4,139
5,863	4,138
5,864	4,137
5,865	4,136

Hour	COUNTDOWN
5,866	4,135
5,867	4,134
5,868	4,133
5,869	4,132
5,870	4,131
5,871	4,130
5,872	4,129
5,873	4,128
5,874	4,127
5,875	4,126
5,876	4,125
5,877	4,124
5,878	4,123
5,879	4,122
5,880	4,121
5,881	4,120
5,882	4,119

Hour	COUNTDOWN
5,883	4,118
5,884	4,117
5,885	4,116
5,886	4,115
5,887	4,114
5,888	4,113
5,889	4,112
5,890	4,111
5,891	4,110
5,892	4,109
5,893	4,108
5,894	4,107
5,895	4,106
5,896	4,105
5,897	4,104
5,898	4,103
5,899	4,102

Hour	COUNTDOWN
5,900	4,101
5,901	4,100
5,902	4,099
5,903	4,098
5,904	4,097
5,905	4,096
5,906	4,095
5,907	4,094
5,908	4,093
5,909	4,092
5,910	4,091
5,911	4,090
5,912	4,089
5,913	4,088
5,914	4,087
5,915	4,086
5,916	4,085

Hour	COUNTDOWN
5,917	4,084
5,918	4,083
5,919	4,082
5,920	4,081
5,921	4,080
5,922	4,079
5,923	4,078
5,924	4,077
5,925	4,076
5,926	4,075
5,927	4,074
5,928	4,073
5,929	4,072
5,930	4,071
5,931	4,070
5,932	4,069
5,933	4,068

Hour	COUNTDOWN
5,934	4,067
5,935	4,066
5,936	4,065
5,937	4,064
5,938	4,063
5,939	4,062
5,940	4,061
5,941	4,060
5,942	4,059
5,943	4,058
5,944	4,057
5,945	4,056
5,946	4,055
5,947	4,054
5,948	4,053
5,949	4,052
5,950	4,051

Hour	COUNTDOWN
5,951	4,050
5,952	4,049
5,953	4,048
5,954	4,047
5,955	4,046
5,956	4,045
5,957	4,044
5,958	4,043
5,959	4,042
5,960	4,041
5,961	4,040
5,962	4,039
5,963	4,038
5,964	4,037
5,965	4,036
5,966	4,035
5,967	4,034

Hour	COUNTDOWN
5,968	4,033
5,969	4,032
5,970	4,031
5,971	4,030
5,972	4,029
5,973	4,028
5,974	4,027
5,975	4,026
5,976	4,025
5,977	4,024
5,978	4,023
5,979	4,022
5,980	4,021
5,981	4,020
5,982	4,019
5,983	4,018
5,984	4,017

Hour	COUNTDOWN
5,985	4,016
5,986	4,015
5,987	4,014
5,988	4,013
5,989	4,012
5,990	4,011
5,991	4,010
5,992	4,009
5,993	4,008
5,994	4,007
5,995	4,006
5,996	4,005
5,997	4,004
5,998	4,003
5,999	4,002
6,000	4,001
6,001	4,000

Hour	COUNTDOWN
6,002	3,999
6,003	3,998
6,004	3,997
6,005	3,996
6,006	3,995
6,007	3,994
6,008	3,993
6,009	3,992
6,010	3,991
6,011	3,990
6,012	3,989
6,013	3,988
6,014	3,987
6,015	3,986
6,016	3,985
6,017	3,984
6,018	3,983

Hour	COUNTDOWN
6,019	3,982
6,020	3,981
6,021	3,980
6,022	3,979
6,023	3,978
6,024	3,977
6,025	3,976
6,026	3,975
6,027	3,974
6,028	3,973
6,029	3,972
6,030	3,971
6,031	3,970
6,032	3,969
6,033	3,968
6,034	3,967
6,035	3,966

Hour	COUNTDOWN
6,036	3,965
6,037	3,964
6,038	3,963
6,039	3,962
6,040	3,961
6,041	3,960
6,042	3,959
6,043	3,958
6,044	3,957
6,045	3,956
6,046	3,955
6,047	3,954
6,048	3,953
6,049	3,952
6,050	3,951
6,051	3,950
6,052	3,949

Hour	COUNTDOWN
6,053	3,948
6,054	3,947
6,055	3,946
6,056	3,945
6,057	3,944
6,058	3,943
6,059	3,942
6,060	3,941
6,061	3,940
6,062	3,939
6,063	3,938
6,064	3,937
6,065	3,936
6,066	3,935
6,067	3,934
6,068	3,933
6,069	3,932

Hour	COUNTDOWN
6,070	3,931
6,071	3,930
6,072	3,929
6,073	3,928
6,074	3,927
6,075	3,926
6,076	3,925
6,077	3,924
6,078	3,923
6,079	3,922
6,080	3,921
6,081	3,920
6,082	3,919
6,083	3,918
6,084	3,917
6,085	3,916
6,086	3,915

Hour	COUNTDOWN
6,087	3,914
6,088	3,913
6,089	3,912
6,090	3,911
6,091	3,910
6,092	3,909
6,093	3,908
6,094	3,907
6,095	3,906
6,096	3,905
6,097	3,904
6,098	3,903
6,099	3,902
6,100	3,901
6,101	3,900
6,102	3,899
6,103	3,898

Hour	COUNTDOWN
6,104	3,897
6,105	3,896
6,106	3,895
6,107	3,894
6,108	3,893
6,109	3,892
6,110	3,891
6,111	3,890
6,112	3,889
6,113	3,888
6,114	3,887
6,115	3,886
6,116	3,885
6,117	3,884
6,118	3,883
6,119	3,882
6,120	3,881

Hour	COUNTDOWN
6,121	3,880
6,122	3,879
6,123	3,878
6,124	3,877
6,125	3,876
6,126	3,875
6,127	3,874
6,128	3,873
6,129	3,872
6,130	3,871
6,131	3,870
6,132	3,869
6,133	3,868
6,134	3,867
6,135	3,866
6,136	3,865
6,137	3,864

Hour	COUNTDOWN
6,138	3,863
6,139	3,862
6,140	3,861
6,141	3,860
6,142	3,859
6,143	3,858
6,144	3,857
6,145	3,856
6,146	3,855
6,147	3,854
6,148	3,853
6,149	3,852
6,150	3,851
6,151	3,850
6,152	3,849
6,153	3,848
6,154	3,847

Hour	COUNTDOWN
6,155	3,846
6,156	3,845
6,157	3,844
6,158	3,843
6,159	3,842
6,160	3,841
6,161	3,840
6,162	3,839
6,163	3,838
6,164	3,837
6,165	3,836
6,166	3,835
6,167	3,834
6,168	3,833
6,169	3,832
6,170	3,831
6,171	3,830

Hour	COUNTDOWN
6,172	3,829
6,173	3,828
6,174	3,827
6,175	3,826
6,176	3,825
6,177	3,824
6,178	3,823
6,179	3,822
6,180	3,821
6,181	3,820
6,182	3,819
6,183	3,818
6,184	3,817
6,185	3,816
6,186	3,815
6,187	3,814
6,188	3,813

Hour	COUNTDOWN
6,189	3,812
6,190	3,811
6,191	3,810
6,192	3,809
6,193	3,808
6,194	3,807
6,195	3,806
6,196	3,805
6,197	3,804
6,198	3,803
6,199	3,802
6,200	3,801
6,201	3,800
6,202	3,799
6,203	3,798
6,204	3,797
6,205	3,796

Hour	COUNTDOWN
6,206	3,795
6,207	3,794
6,208	3,793
6,209	3,792
6,210	3,791
6,211	3,790
6,212	3,789
6,213	3,788
6,214	3,787
6,215	3,786
6,216	3,785
6,217	3,784
6,218	3,783
6,219	3,782
6,220	3,781
6,221	3,780
6,222	3,779

Hour	COUNTDOWN
6,223	3,778
6,224	3,777
6,225	3,776
6,226	3,775
6,227	3,774
6,228	3,773
6,229	3,772
6,230	3,771
6,231	3,770
6,232	3,769
6,233	3,768
6,234	3,767
6,235	3,766
6,236	3,765
6,237	3,764
6,238	3,763
6,239	3,762

Hour	COUNTDOWN
6,240	3,761
6,241	3,760
6,242	3,759
6,243	3,758
6,244	3,757
6,245	3,756
6,246	3,755
6,247	3,754
6,248	3,753
6,249	3,752
6,250	3,751
6,251	3,750
6,252	3,749
6,253	3,748
6,254	3,747
6,255	3,746
6,256	3,745

Hour	COUNTDOWN
6,257	3,744
6,258	3,743
6,259	3,742
6,260	3,741
6,261	3,740
6,262	3,739
6,263	3,738
6,264	3,737
6,265	3,736
6,266	3,735
6,267	3,734
6,268	3,733
6,269	3,732
6,270	3,731
6,271	3,730
6,272	3,729
6,273	3,728

Hour	COUNTDOWN
6,274	3,727
6,275	3,726
6,276	3,725
6,277	3,724
6,278	3,723
6,279	3,722
6,280	3,721
6,281	3,720
6,282	3,719
6,283	3,718
6,284	3,717
6,285	3,716
6,286	3,715
6,287	3,714
6,288	3,713
6,289	3,712
6,290	3,711

Hour	COUNTDOWN
6,291	3,710
6,292	3,709
6,293	3,708
6,294	3,707
6,295	3,706
6,296	3,705
6,297	3,704
6,298	3,703
6,299	3,702
6,300	3,701
6,301	3,700
6,302	3,699
6,303	3,698
6,304	3,697
6,305	3,696
6,306	3,695
6,307	3,694

Hour	COUNTDOWN
6,308	3,693
6,309	3,692
6,310	3,691
6,311	3,690
6,312	3,689
6,313	3,688
6,314	3,687
6,315	3,686
6,316	3,685
6,317	3,684
6,318	3,683
6,319	3,682
6,320	3,681
6,321	3,680
6,322	3,679
6,323	3,678
6,324	3,677

Hour	COUNTDOWN
6,325	3,676
6,326	3,675
6,327	3,674
6,328	3,673
6,329	3,672
6,330	3,671
6,331	3,670
6,332	3,669
6,333	3,668
6,334	3,667
6,335	3,666
6,336	3,665
6,337	3,664
6,338	3,663
6,339	3,662
6,340	3,661
6,341	3,660

Hour	COUNTDOWN
6,342	3,659
6,343	3,658
6,344	3,657
6,345	3,656
6,346	3,655
6,347	3,654
6,348	3,653
6,349	3,652
6,350	3,651
6,351	3,650
6,352	3,649
6,353	3,648
6,354	3,647
6,355	3,646
6,356	3,645
6,357	3,644
6,358	3,643

Hour	COUNTDOWN
6,359	3,642
6,360	3,641
6,361	3,640
6,362	3,639
6,363	3,638
6,364	3,637
6,365	3,636
6,366	3,635
6,367	3,634
6,368	3,633
6,369	3,632
6,370	3,631
6,371	3,630
6,372	3,629
6,373	3,628
6,374	3,627
6,375	3,626

Hour	COUNTDOWN
6,376	3,625
6,377	3,624
6,378	3,623
6,379	3,622
6,380	3,621
6,381	3,620
6,382	3,619
6,383	3,618
6,384	3,617
6,385	3,616
6,386	3,615
6,387	3,614
6,388	3,613
6,389	3,612
6,390	3,611
6,391	3,610
6,392	3,609

Hour	COUNTDOWN
6,393	3,608
6,394	3,607
6,395	3,606
6,396	3,605
6,397	3,604
6,398	3,603
6,399	3,602
6,400	3,601
6,401	3,600
6,402	3,599
6,403	3,598
6,404	3,597
6,405	3,596
6,406	3,595
6,407	3,594
6,408	3,593
6,409	3,592

Hour	COUNTDOWN
6,410	3,591
6,411	3,590
6,412	3,589
6,413	3,588
6,414	3,587
6,415	3,586
6,416	3,585
6,417	3,584
6,418	3,583
6,419	3,582
6,420	3,581
6,421	3,580
6,422	3,579
6,423	3,578
6,424	3,577
6,425	3,576
6,426	3,575

Hour	COUNTDOWN
6,427	3,574
6,428	3,573
6,429	3,572
6,430	3,571
6,431	3,570
6,432	3,569
6,433	3,568
6,434	3,567
6,435	3,566
6,436	3,565
6,437	3,564
6,438	3,563
6,439	3,562
6,440	3,561
6,441	3,560
6,442	3,559
6,443	3,558

Hour	COUNTDOWN
6,444	3,557
6,445	3,556
6,446	3,555
6,447	3,554
6,448	3,553
6,449	3,552
6,450	3,551
6,451	3,550
6,452	3,549
6,453	3,548
6,454	3,547
6,455	3,546
6,456	3,545
6,457	3,544
6,458	3,543
6,459	3,542
6,460	3,541

Hour	COUNTDOWN
6,461	3,540
6,462	3,539
6,463	3,538
6,464	3,537
6,465	3,536
6,466	3,535
6,467	3,534
6,468	3,533
6,469	3,532
6,470	3,531
6,471	3,530
6,472	3,529
6,473	3,528
6,474	3,527
6,475	3,526
6,476	3,525
6,477	3,524

Hour	COUNTDOWN
6,478	3,523
6,479	3,522
6,480	3,521
6,481	3,520
6,482	3,519
6,483	3,518
6,484	3,517
6,485	3,516
6,486	3,515
6,487	3,514
6,488	3,513
6,489	3,512
6,490	3,511
6,491	3,510
6,492	3,509
6,493	3,508
6,494	3,507

Hour	COUNTDOWN
6,495	3,506
6,496	3,505
6,497	3,504
6,498	3,503
6,499	3,502
6,500	3,501
6,501	3,500
6,502	3,499
6,503	3,498
6,504	3,497
6,505	3,496
6,506	3,495
6,507	3,494
6,508	3,493
6,509	3,492
6,510	3,491
6,511	3,490

Hour	COUNTDOWN
6,512	3,489
6,513	3,488
6,514	3,487
6,515	3,486
6,516	3,485
6,517	3,484
6,518	3,483
6,519	3,482
6,520	3,481
6,521	3,480
6,522	3,479
6,523	3,478
6,524	3,477
6,525	3,476
6,526	3,475
6,527	3,474
6,528	3,473

Hour	COUNTDOWN
6,529	3,472
6,530	3,471
6,531	3,470
6,532	3,469
6,533	3,468
6,534	3,467
6,535	3,466
6,536	3,465
6,537	3,464
6,538	3,463
6,539	3,462
6,540	3,461
6,541	3,460
6,542	3,459
6,543	3,458
6,544	3,457
6,545	3,456

Hour	COUNTDOWN
6,546	3,455
6,547	3,454
6,548	3,453
6,549	3,452
6,550	3,451
6,551	3,450
6,552	3,449
6,553	3,448
6,554	3,447
6,555	3,446
6,556	3,445
6,557	3,444
6,558	3,443
6,559	3,442
6,560	3,441
6,561	3,440
6,562	3,439

Hour	COUNTDOWN
6,563	3,438
6,564	3,437
6,565	3,436
6,566	3,435
6,567	3,434
6,568	3,433
6,569	3,432
6,570	3,431
6,571	3,430
6,572	3,429
6,573	3,428
6,574	3,427
6,575	3,426
6,576	3,425
6,577	3,424
6,578	3,423
6,579	3,422

Hour	COUNTDOWN
6,580	3,421
6,581	3,420
6,582	3,419
6,583	3,418
6,584	3,417
6,585	3,416
6,586	3,415
6,587	3,414
6,588	3,413
6,589	3,412
6,590	3,411
6,591	3,410
6,592	3,409
6,593	3,408
6,594	3,407
6,595	3,406
6,596	3,405

Hour	COUNTDOWN
6,597	3,404
6,598	3,403
6,599	3,402
6,600	3,401
6,601	3,400
6,602	3,399
6,603	3,398
6,604	3,397
6,605	3,396
6,606	3,395
6,607	3,394
6,608	3,393
6,609	3,392
6,610	3,391
6,611	3,390
6,612	3,389
6,613	3,388

Hour	COUNTDOWN
6,614	3,387
6,615	3,386
6,616	3,385
6,617	3,384
6,618	3,383
6,619	3,382
6,620	3,381
6,621	3,380
6,622	3,379
6,623	3,378
6,624	3,377
6,625	3,376
6,626	3,375
6,627	3,374
6,628	3,373
6,629	3,372
6,630	3,371

Hour	COUNTDOWN
6,631	3,370
6,632	3,369
6,633	3,368
6,634	3,367
6,635	3,366
6,636	3,365
6,637	3,364
6,638	3,363
6,639	3,362
6,640	3,361
6,641	3,360
6,642	3,359
6,643	3,358
6,644	3,357
6,645	3,356
6,646	3,355
6,647	3,354

Hour	COUNTDOWN
6,648	3,353
6,649	3,352
6,650	3,351
6,651	3,350
6,652	3,349
6,653	3,348
6,654	3,347
6,655	3,346
6,656	3,345
6,657	3,344
6,658	3,343
6,659	3,342
6,660	3,341
6,661	3,340
6,662	3,339
6,663	3,338
6,664	3,337

Hour	COUNTDOWN
6,665	3,336
6,666	3,335
6,667	3,334
6,668	3,333
6,669	3,332
6,670	3,331
6,671	3,330
6,672	3,329
6,673	3,328
6,674	3,327
6,675	3,326
6,676	3,325
6,677	3,324
6,678	3,323
6,679	3,322
6,680	3,321
6,681	3,320

Hour	COUNTDOWN
6,682	3,319
6,683	3,318
6,684	3,317
6,685	3,316
6,686	3,315
6,687	3,314
6,688	3,313
6,689	3,312
6,690	3,311
6,691	3,310
6,692	3,309
6,693	3,308
6,694	3,307
6,695	3,306
6,696	3,305
6,697	3,304
6,698	3,303

Hour	COUNTDOWN
6,699	3,302
6,700	3,301
6,701	3,300
6,702	3,299
6,703	3,298
6,704	3,297
6,705	3,296
6,706	3,295
6,707	3,294
6,708	3,293
6,709	3,292
6,710	3,291
6,711	3,290
6,712	3,289
6,713	3,288
6,714	3,287
6,715	3,286

Hour	COUNTDOWN
6,716	3,285
6,717	3,284
6,718	3,283
6,719	3,282
6,720	3,281
6,721	3,280
6,722	3,279
6,723	3,278
6,724	3,277
6,725	3,276
6,726	3,275
6,727	3,274
6,728	3,273
6,729	3,272
6,730	3,271
6,731	3,270
6,732	3,269

Hour	COUNTDOWN
6,733	3,268
6,734	3,267
6,735	3,266
6,736	3,265
6,737	3,264
6,738	3,263
6,739	3,262
6,740	3,261
6,741	3,260
6,742	3,259
6,743	3,258
6,744	3,257
6,745	3,256
6,746	3,255
6,747	3,254
6,748	3,253
6,749	3,252

Hour	COUNTDOWN
6,750	3,251
6,751	3,250
6,752	3,249
6,753	3,248
6,754	3,247
6,755	3,246
6,756	3,245
6,757	3,244
6,758	3,243
6,759	3,242
6,760	3,241
6,761	3,240
6,762	3,239
6,763	3,238
6,764	3,237
6,765	3,236
6,766	3,235

Hour	COUNTDOWN
6,767	3,234
6,768	3,233
6,769	3,232
6,770	3,231
6,771	3,230
6,772	3,229
6,773	3,228
6,774	3,227
6,775	3,226
6,776	3,225
6,777	3,224
6,778	3,223
6,779	3,222
6,780	3,221
6,781	3,220
6,782	3,219
6,783	3,218

Hour	COUNTDOWN
6,784	3,217
6,785	3,216
6,786	3,215
6,787	3,214
6,788	3,213
6,789	3,212
6,790	3,211
6,791	3,210
6,792	3,209
6,793	3,208
6,794	3,207
6,795	3,206
6,796	3,205
6,797	3,204
6,798	3,203
6,799	3,202
6,800	3,201

Hour	COUNTDOWN
6,801	3,200
6,802	3,199
6,803	3,198
6,804	3,197
6,805	3,196
6,806	3,195
6,807	3,194
6,808	3,193
6,809	3,192
6,810	3,191
6,811	3,190
6,812	3,189
6,813	3,188
6,814	3,187
6,815	3,186
6,816	3,185
6,817	3,184

Hour	COUNTDOWN
6,818	3,183
6,819	3,182
6,820	3,181
6,821	3,180
6,822	3,179
6,823	3,178
6,824	3,177
6,825	3,176
6,826	3,175
6,827	3,174
6,828	3,173
6,829	3,172
6,830	3,171
6,831	3,170
6,832	3,169
6,833	3,168
6,834	3,167

Hour	COUNTDOWN
6,835	3,166
6,836	3,165
6,837	3,164
6,838	3,163
6,839	3,162
6,840	3,161
6,841	3,160
6,842	3,159
6,843	3,158
6,844	3,157
6,845	3,156
6,846	3,155
6,847	3,154
6,848	3,153
6,849	3,152
6,850	3,151
6,851	3,150

Hour	COUNTDOWN
6,852	3,149
6,853	3,148
6,854	3,147
6,855	3,146
6,856	3,145
6,857	3,144
6,858	3,143
6,859	3,142
6,860	3,141
6,861	3,140
6,862	3,139
6,863	3,138
6,864	3,137
6,865	3,136
6,866	3,135
6,867	3,134
6,868	3,133

Hour	COUNTDOWN
6,869	3,132
6,870	3,131
6,871	3,130
6,872	3,129
6,873	3,128
6,874	3,127
6,875	3,126
6,876	3,125
6,877	3,124
6,878	3,123
6,879	3,122
6,880	3,121
6,881	3,120
6,882	3,119
6,883	3,118
6,884	3,117
6,885	3,116

Hour	COUNTDOWN
6,886	3,115
6,887	3,114
6,888	3,113
6,889	3,112
6,890	3,111
6,891	3,110
6,892	3,109
6,893	3,108
6,894	3,107
6,895	3,106
6,896	3,105
6,897	3,104
6,898	3,103
6,899	3,102
6,900	3,101
6,901	3,100
6,902	3,099

Hour	COUNTDOWN
6,903	3,098
6,904	3,097
6,905	3,096
6,906	3,095
6,907	3,094
6,908	3,093
6,909	3,092
6,910	3,091
6,911	3,090
6,912	3,089
6,913	3,088
6,914	3,087
6,915	3,086
6,916	3,085
6,917	3,084
6,918	3,083
6,919	3,082

Hour	COUNTDOWN
6,920	3,081
6,921	3,080
6,922	3,079
6,923	3,078
6,924	3,077
6,925	3,076
6,926	3,075
6,927	3,074
6,928	3,073
6,929	3,072
6,930	3,071
6,931	3,070
6,932	3,069
6,933	3,068
6,934	3,067
6,935	3,066
6,936	3,065

Hour	COUNTDOWN
6,937	3,064
6,938	3,063
6,939	3,062
6,940	3,061
6,941	3,060
6,942	3,059
6,943	3,058
6,944	3,057
6,945	3,056
6,946	3,055
6,947	3,054
6,948	3,053
6,949	3,052
6,950	3,051
6,951	3,050
6,952	3,049
6,953	3,048

Hour	COUNTDOWN
6,954	3,047
6,955	3,046
6,956	3,045
6,957	3,044
6,958	3,043
6,959	3,042
6,960	3,041
6,961	3,040
6,962	3,039
6,963	3,038
6,964	3,037
6,965	3,036
6,966	3,035
6,967	3,034
6,968	3,033
6,969	3,032
6,970	3,031

Hour	COUNTDOWN
6,971	3,030
6,972	3,029
6,973	3,028
6,974	3,027
6,975	3,026
6,976	3,025
6,977	3,024
6,978	3,023
6,979	3,022
6,980	3,021
6,981	3,020
6,982	3,019
6,983	3,018
6,984	3,017
6,985	3,016
6,986	3,015
6,987	3,014

Hour	COUNTDOWN
6,988	3,013
6,989	3,012
6,990	3,011
6,991	3,010
6,992	3,009
6,993	3,008
6,994	3,007
6,995	3,006
6,996	3,005
6,997	3,004
6,998	3,003
6,999	3,002
7,000	3,001
7,001	3,000
7,002	2,999
7,003	2,998
7,004	2,997

Hour	COUNTDOWN
7,005	2,996
7,006	2,995
7,007	2,994
7,008	2,993
7,009	2,992
7,010	2,991
7,011	2,990
7,012	2,989
7,013	2,988
7,014	2,987
7,015	2,986
7,016	2,985
7,017	2,984
7,018	2,983
7,019	2,982
7,020	2,981
7,021	2,980

Hour	COUNTDOWN
7,022	2,979
7,023	2,978
7,024	2,977
7,025	2,976
7,026	2,975
7,027	2,974
7,028	2,973
7,029	2,972
7,030	2,971
7,031	2,970
7,032	2,969
7,033	2,968
7,034	2,967
7,035	2,966
7,036	2,965
7,037	2,964
7,038	2,963

Hour	COUNTDOWN
7,039	2,962
7,040	2,961
7,041	2,960
7,042	2,959
7,043	2,958
7,044	2,957
7,045	2,956
7,046	2,955
7,047	2,954
7,048	2,953
7,049	2,952
7,050	2,951
7,051	2,950
7,052	2,949
7,053	2,948
7,054	2,947
7,055	2,946

Hour	COUNTDOWN
7,056	2,945
7,057	2,944
7,058	2,943
7,059	2,942
7,060	2,941
7,061	2,940
7,062	2,939
7,063	2,938
7,064	2,937
7,065	2,936
7,066	2,935
7,067	2,934
7,068	2,933
7,069	2,932
7,070	2,931
7,071	2,930
7,072	2,929

Hour	COUNTDOWN
7,073	2,928
7,074	2,927
7,075	2,926
7,076	2,925
7,077	2,924
7,078	2,923
7,079	2,922
7,080	2,921
7,081	2,920
7,082	2,919
7,083	2,918
7,084	2,917
7,085	2,916
7,086	2,915
7,087	2,914
7,088	2,913
7,089	2,912

Hour	COUNTDOWN
7,090	2,911
7,091	2,910
7,092	2,909
7,093	2,908
7,094	2,907
7,095	2,906
7,096	2,905
7,097	2,904
7,098	2,903
7,099	2,902
7,100	2,901
7,101	2,900
7,102	2,899
7,103	2,898
7,104	2,897
7,105	2,896
7,106	2,895

Hour	COUNTDOWN
7,107	2,894
7,108	2,893
7,109	2,892
7,110	2,891
7,111	2,890
7,112	2,889
7,113	2,888
7,114	2,887
7,115	2,886
7,116	2,885
7,117	2,884
7,118	2,883
7,119	2,882
7,120	2,881
7,121	2,880
7,122	2,879
7,123	2,878

Hour	COUNTDOWN
7,124	2,877
7,125	2,876
7,126	2,875
7,127	2,874
7,128	2,873
7,129	2,872
7,130	2,871
7,131	2,870
7,132	2,869
7,133	2,868
7,134	2,867
7,135	2,866
7,136	2,865
7,137	2,864
7,138	2,863
7,139	2,862
7,140	2,861

Hour	COUNTDOWN
7,141	2,860
7,142	2,859
7,143	2,858
7,144	2,857
7,145	2,856
7,146	2,855
7,147	2,854
7,148	2,853
7,149	2,852
7,150	2,851
7,151	2,850
7,152	2,849
7,153	2,848
7,154	2,847
7,155	2,846
7,156	2,845
7,157	2,844

Hour	COUNTDOWN
7,158	2,843
7,159	2,842
7,160	2,841
7,161	2,840
7,162	2,839
7,163	2,838
7,164	2,837
7,165	2,836
7,166	2,835
7,167	2,834
7,168	2,833
7,169	2,832
7,170	2,831
7,171	2,830
7,172	2,829
7,173	2,828
7,174	2,827

Hour	COUNTDOWN
7,175	2,826
7,176	2,825
7,177	2,824
7,178	2,823
7,179	2,822
7,180	2,821
7,181	2,820
7,182	2,819
7,183	2,818
7,184	2,817
7,185	2,816
7,186	2,815
7,187	2,814
7,188	2,813
7,189	2,812
7,190	2,811
7,191	2,810

Hour	COUNTDOWN
7,192	2,809
7,193	2,808
7,194	2,807
7,195	2,806
7,196	2,805
7,197	2,804
7,198	2,803
7,199	2,802
7,200	2,801
7,201	2,800
7,202	2,799
7,203	2,798
7,204	2,797
7,205	2,796
7,206	2,795
7,207	2,794
7,208	2,793

Hour	COUNTDOWN
7,209	2,792
7,210	2,791
7,211	2,790
7,212	2,789
7,213	2,788
7,214	2,787
7,215	2,786
7,216	2,785
7,217	2,784
7,218	2,783
7,219	2,782
7,220	2,781
7,221	2,780
7,222	2,779
7,223	2,778
7,224	2,777
7,225	2,776

Hour	COUNTDOWN
7,226	2,775
7,227	2,774
7,228	2,773
7,229	2,772
7,230	2,771
7,231	2,770
7,232	2,769
7,233	2,768
7,234	2,767
7,235	2,766
7,236	2,765
7,237	2,764
7,238	2,763
7,239	2,762
7,240	2,761
7,241	2,760
7,242	2,759

Hour	COUNTDOWN
7,243	2,758
7,244	2,757
7,245	2,756
7,246	2,755
7,247	2,754
7,248	2,753
7,249	2,752
7,250	2,751
7,251	2,750
7,252	2,749
7,253	2,748
7,254	2,747
7,255	2,746
7,256	2,745
7,257	2,744
7,258	2,743
7,259	2,742

Hour	COUNTDOWN
7,260	2,741
7,261	2,740
7,262	2,739
7,263	2,738
7,264	2,737
7,265	2,736
7,266	2,735
7,267	2,734
7,268	2,733
7,269	2,732
7,270	2,731
7,271	2,730
7,272	2,729
7,273	2,728
7,274	2,727
7,275	2,726
7,276	2,725

Hour	COUNTDOWN
7,277	2,724
7,278	2,723
7,279	2,722
7,280	2,721
7,281	2,720
7,282	2,719
7,283	2,718
7,284	2,717
7,285	2,716
7,286	2,715
7,287	2,714
7,288	2,713
7,289	2,712
7,290	2,711
7,291	2,710
7,292	2,709
7,293	2,708

Hour	COUNTDOWN
7,294	2,707
7,295	2,706
7,296	2,705
7,297	2,704
7,298	2,703
7,299	2,702
7,300	2,701
7,301	2,700
7,302	2,699
7,303	2,698
7,304	2,697
7,305	2,696
7,306	2,695
7,307	2,694
7,308	2,693
7,309	2,692
7,310	2,691

Hour	COUNTDOWN
7,311	2,690
7,312	2,689
7,313	2,688
7,314	2,687
7,315	2,686
7,316	2,685
7,317	2,684
7,318	2,683
7,319	2,682
7,320	2,681
7,321	2,680
7,322	2,679
7,323	2,678
7,324	2,677
7,325	2,676
7,326	2,675
7,327	2,674

Hour	COUNTDOWN
7,328	2,673
7,329	2,672
7,330	2,671
7,331	2,670
7,332	2,669
7,333	2,668
7,334	2,667
7,335	2,666
7,336	2,665
7,337	2,664
7,338	2,663
7,339	2,662
7,340	2,661
7,341	2,660
7,342	2,659
7,343	2,658
7,344	2,657

Hour	COUNTDOWN
7,345	2,656
7,346	2,655
7,347	2,654
7,348	2,653
7,349	2,652
7,350	2,651
7,351	2,650
7,352	2,649
7,353	2,648
7,354	2,647
7,355	2,646
7,356	2,645
7,357	2,644
7,358	2,643
7,359	2,642
7,360	2,641
7,361	2,640

Hour	COUNTDOWN
7,362	2,639
7,363	2,638
7,364	2,637
7,365	2,636
7,366	2,635
7,367	2,634
7,368	2,633
7,369	2,632
7,370	2,631
7,371	2,630
7,372	2,629
7,373	2,628
7,374	2,627
7,375	2,626
7,376	2,625
7,377	2,624
7,378	2,623

Hour	COUNTDOWN
7,379	2,622
7,380	2,621
7,381	2,620
7,382	2,619
7,383	2,618
7,384	2,617
7,385	2,616
7,386	2,615
7,387	2,614
7,388	2,613
7,389	2,612
7,390	2,611
7,391	2,610
7,392	2,609
7,393	2,608
7,394	2,607
7,395	2,606

Hour	COUNTDOWN
7,396	2,605
7,397	2,604
7,398	2,603
7,399	2,602
7,400	2,601
7,401	2,600
7,402	2,599
7,403	2,598
7,404	2,597
7,405	2,596
7,406	2,595
7,407	2,594
7,408	2,593
7,409	2,592
7,410	2,591
7,411	2,590
7,412	2,589

Hour	COUNTDOWN
7,413	2,588
7,414	2,587
7,415	2,586
7,416	2,585
7,417	2,584
7,418	2,583
7,419	2,582
7,420	2,581
7,421	2,580
7,422	2,579
7,423	2,578
7,424	2,577
7,425	2,576
7,426	2,575
7,427	2,574
7,428	2,573
7,429	2,572

Hour	COUNTDOWN
7,430	2,571
7,431	2,570
7,432	2,569
7,433	2,568
7,434	2,567
7,435	2,566
7,436	2,565
7,437	2,564
7,438	2,563
7,439	2,562
7,440	2,561
7,441	2,560
7,442	2,559
7,443	2,558
7,444	2,557
7,445	2,556
7,446	2,555

Hour	COUNTDOWN
7,447	2,554
7,448	2,553
7,449	2,552
7,450	2,551
7,451	2,550
7,452	2,549
7,453	2,548
7,454	2,547
7,455	2,546
7,456	2,545
7,457	2,544
7,458	2,543
7,459	2,542
7,460	2,541
7,461	2,540
7,462	2,539
7,463	2,538

Hour	COUNTDOWN
7,464	2,537
7,465	2,536
7,466	2,535
7,467	2,534
7,468	2,533
7,469	2,532
7,470	2,531
7,471	2,530
7,472	2,529
7,473	2,528
7,474	2,527
7,475	2,526
7,476	2,525
7,477	2,524
7,478	2,523
7,479	2,522
7,480	2,521

Hour	COUNTDOWN
7,481	2,520
7,482	2,519
7,483	2,518
7,484	2,517
7,485	2,516
7,486	2,515
7,487	2,514
7,488	2,513
7,489	2,512
7,490	2,511
7,491	2,510
7,492	2,509
7,493	2,508
7,494	2,507
7,495	2,506
7,496	2,505
7,497	2,504

Hour	COUNTDOWN
7,498	2,503
7,499	2,502
7,500	2,501
7,501	2,500
7,502	2,499
7,503	2,498
7,504	2,497
7,505	2,496
7,506	2,495
7,507	2,494
7,508	2,493
7,509	2,492
7,510	2,491
7,511	2,490
7,512	2,489
7,513	2,488
7,514	2,487

Hour	COUNTDOWN
7,515	2,486
7,516	2,485
7,517	2,484
7,518	2,483
7,519	2,482
7,520	2,481
7,521	2,480
7,522	2,479
7,523	2,478
7,524	2,477
7,525	2,476
7,526	2,475
7,527	2,474
7,528	2,473
7,529	2,472
7,530	2,471
7,531	2,470

Hour	COUNTDOWN
7,532	2,469
7,533	2,468
7,534	2,467
7,535	2,466
7,536	2,465
7,537	2,464
7,538	2,463
7,539	2,462
7,540	2,461
7,541	2,460
7,542	2,459
7,543	2,458
7,544	2,457
7,545	2,456
7,546	2,455
7,547	2,454
7,548	2,453

Hour	COUNTDOWN
7,549	2,452
7,550	2,451
7,551	2,450
7,552	2,449
7,553	2,448
7,554	2,447
7,555	2,446
7,556	2,445
7,557	2,444
7,558	2,443
7,559	2,442
7,560	2,441
7,561	2,440
7,562	2,439
7,563	2,438
7,564	2,437
7,565	2,436

Hour	COUNTDOWN
7,566	2,435
7,567	2,434
7,568	2,433
7,569	2,432
7,570	2,431
7,571	2,430
7,572	2,429
7,573	2,428
7,574	2,427
7,575	2,426
7,576	2,425
7,577	2,424
7,578	2,423
7,579	2,422
7,580	2,421
7,581	2,420
7,582	2,419

Hour	COUNTDOWN
7,583	2,418
7,584	2,417
7,585	2,416
7,586	2,415
7,587	2,414
7,588	2,413
7,589	2,412
7,590	2,411
7,591	2,410
7,592	2,409
7,593	2,408
7,594	2,407
7,595	2,406
7,596	2,405
7,597	2,404
7,598	2,403
7,599	2,402

Hour	COUNTDOWN
7,600	2,401
7,601	2,400
7,602	2,399
7,603	2,398
7,604	2,397
7,605	2,396
7,606	2,395
7,607	2,394
7,608	2,393
7,609	2,392
7,610	2,391
7,611	2,390
7,612	2,389
7,613	2,388
7,614	2,387
7,615	2,386
7,616	2,385

Hour	COUNTDOWN
7,617	2,384
7,618	2,383
7,619	2,382
7,620	2,381
7,621	2,380
7,622	2,379
7,623	2,378
7,624	2,377
7,625	2,376
7,626	2,375
7,627	2,374
7,628	2,373
7,629	2,372
7,630	2,371
7,631	2,370
7,632	2,369
7,633	2,368

Hour	COUNTDOWN
7,634	2,367
7,635	2,366
7,636	2,365
7,637	2,364
7,638	2,363
7,639	2,362
7,640	2,361
7,641	2,360
7,642	2,359
7,643	2,358
7,644	2,357
7,645	2,356
7,646	2,355
7,647	2,354
7,648	2,353
7,649	2,352
7,650	2,351

Hour	COUNTDOWN
7,651	2,350
7,652	2,349
7,653	2,348
7,654	2,347
7,655	2,346
7,656	2,345
7,657	2,344
7,658	2,343
7,659	2,342
7,660	2,341
7,661	2,340
7,662	2,339
7,663	2,338
7,664	2,337
7,665	2,336
7,666	2,335
7,667	2,334

Hour	COUNTDOWN
7,668	2,333
7,669	2,332
7,670	2,331
7,671	2,330
7,672	2,329
7,673	2,328
7,674	2,327
7,675	2,326
7,676	2,325
7,677	2,324
7,678	2,323
7,679	2,322
7,680	2,321
7,681	2,320
7,682	2,319
7,683	2,318
7,684	2,317

Hour	COUNTDOWN
7,685	2,316
7,686	2,315
7,687	2,314
7,688	2,313
7,689	2,312
7,690	2,311
7,691	2,310
7,692	2,309
7,693	2,308
7,694	2,307
7,695	2,306
7,696	2,305
7,697	2,304
7,698	2,303
7,699	2,302
7,700	2,301
7,701	2,300

Hour	COUNTDOWN
7,702	2,299
7,703	2,298
7,704	2,297
7,705	2,296
7,706	2,295
7,707	2,294
7,708	2,293
7,709	2,292
7,710	2,291
7,711	2,290
7,712	2,289
7,713	2,288
7,714	2,287
7,715	2,286
7,716	2,285
7,717	2,284
7,718	2,283

Hour	COUNTDOWN
7,719	2,282
7,720	2,281
7,721	2,280
7,722	2,279
7,723	2,278
7,724	2,277
7,725	2,276
7,726	2,275
7,727	2,274
7,728	2,273
7,729	2,272
7,730	2,271
7,731	2,270
7,732	2,269
7,733	2,268
7,734	2,267
7,735	2,266

Hour	COUNTDOWN
7,736	2,265
7,737	2,264
7,738	2,263
7,739	2,262
7,740	2,261
7,741	2,260
7,742	2,259
7,743	2,258
7,744	2,257
7,745	2,256
7,746	2,255
7,747	2,254
7,748	2,253
7,749	2,252
7,750	2,251
7,751	2,250
7,752	2,249

Hour	COUNTDOWN
7,753	2,248
7,754	2,247
7,755	2,246
7,756	2,245
7,757	2,244
7,758	2,243
7,759	2,242
7,760	2,241
7,761	2,240
7,762	2,239
7,763	2,238
7,764	2,237
7,765	2,236
7,766	2,235
7,767	2,234
7,768	2,233
7,769	2,232

Hour	COUNTDOWN
7,770	2,231
7,771	2,230
7,772	2,229
7,773	2,228
7,774	2,227
7,775	2,226
7,776	2,225
7,777	2,224
7,778	2,223
7,779	2,222
7,780	2,221
7,781	2,220
7,782	2,219
7,783	2,218
7,784	2,217
7,785	2,216
7,786	2,215

Hour	COUNTDOWN
7,787	2,214
7,788	2,213
7,789	2,212
7,790	2,211
7,791	2,210
7,792	2,209
7,793	2,208
7,794	2,207
7,795	2,206
7,796	2,205
7,797	2,204
7,798	2,203
7,799	2,202
7,800	2,201
7,801	2,200
7,802	2,199
7,803	2,198

Hour	COUNTDOWN
7,804	2,197
7,805	2,196
7,806	2,195
7,807	2,194
7,808	2,193
7,809	2,192
7,810	2,191
7,811	2,190
7,812	2,189
7,813	2,188
7,814	2,187
7,815	2,186
7,816	2,185
7,817	2,184
7,818	2,183
7,819	2,182
7,820	2,181

Hour	COUNTDOWN
7,821	2,180
7,822	2,179
7,823	2,178
7,824	2,177
7,825	2,176
7,826	2,175
7,827	2,174
7,828	2,173
7,829	2,172
7,830	2,171
7,831	2,170
7,832	2,169
7,833	2,168
7,834	2,167
7,835	2,166
7,836	2,165
7,837	2,164

Hour	COUNTDOWN
7,838	2,163
7,839	2,162
7,840	2,161
7,841	2,160
7,842	2,159
7,843	2,158
7,844	2,157
7,845	2,156
7,846	2,155
7,847	2,154
7,848	2,153
7,849	2,152
7,850	2,151
7,851	2,150
7,852	2,149
7,853	2,148
7,854	2,147

Hour	COUNTDOWN
7,855	2,146
7,856	2,145
7,857	2,144
7,858	2,143
7,859	2,142
7,860	2,141
7,861	2,140
7,862	2,139
7,863	2,138
7,864	2,137
7,865	2,136
7,866	2,135
7,867	2,134
7,868	2,133
7,869	2,132
7,870	2,131
7,871	2,130

Hour	COUNTDOWN
7,872	2,129
7,873	2,128
7,874	2,127
7,875	2,126
7,876	2,125
7,877	2,124
7,878	2,123
7,879	2,122
7,880	2,121
7,881	2,120
7,882	2,119
7,883	2,118
7,884	2,117
7,885	2,116
7,886	2,115
7,887	2,114
7,888	2,113

Hour	COUNTDOWN
7,889	2,112
7,890	2,111
7,891	2,110
7,892	2,109
7,893	2,108
7,894	2,107
7,895	2,106
7,896	2,105
7,897	2,104
7,898	2,103
7,899	2,102
7,900	2,101
7,901	2,100
7,902	2,099
7,903	2,098
7,904	2,097
7,905	2,096

Hour	COUNTDOWN
7,906	2,095
7,907	2,094
7,908	2,093
7,909	2,092
7,910	2,091
7,911	2,090
7,912	2,089
7,913	2,088
7,914	2,087
7,915	2,086
7,916	2,085
7,917	2,084
7,918	2,083
7,919	2,082
7,920	2,081
7,921	2,080
7,922	2,079

Hour	COUNTDOWN
7,923	2,078
7,924	2,077
7,925	2,076
7,926	2,075
7,927	2,074
7,928	2,073
7,929	2,072
7,930	2,071
7,931	2,070
7,932	2,069
7,933	2,068
7,934	2,067
7,935	2,066
7,936	2,065
7,937	2,064
7,938	2,063
7,939	2,062

Hour	COUNTDOWN
7,940	2,061
7,941	2,060
7,942	2,059
7,943	2,058
7,944	2,057
7,945	2,056
7,946	2,055
7,947	2,054
7,948	2,053
7,949	2,052
7,950	2,051
7,951	2,050
7,952	2,049
7,953	2,048
7,954	2,047
7,955	2,046
7,956	2,045

Hour	COUNTDOWN
7,957	2,044
7,958	2,043
7,959	2,042
7,960	2,041
7,961	2,040
7,962	2,039
7,963	2,038
7,964	2,037
7,965	2,036
7,966	2,035
7,967	2,034
7,968	2,033
7,969	2,032
7,970	2,031
7,971	2,030
7,972	2,029
7,973	2,028

Hour	COUNTDOWN
7,974	2,027
7,975	2,026
7,976	2,025
7,977	2,024
7,978	2,023
7,979	2,022
7,980	2,021
7,981	2,020
7,982	2,019
7,983	2,018
7,984	2,017
7,985	2,016
7,986	2,015
7,987	2,014
7,988	2,013
7,989	2,012
7,990	2,011

Hour	COUNTDOWN
7,991	2,010
7,992	2,009
7,993	2,008
7,994	2,007
7,995	2,006
7,996	2,005
7,997	2,004
7,998	2,003
7,999	2,002
8,000	2,001
8,001	2,000
8,002	1,999
8,003	1,998
8,004	1,997
8,005	1,996
8,006	1,995
8,007	1,994

Hour	COUNTDOWN
8,008	1,993
8,009	1,992
8,010	1,991
8,011	1,990
8,012	1,989
8,013	1,988
8,014	1,987
8,015	1,986
8,016	1,985
8,017	1,984
8,018	1,983
8,019	1,982
8,020	1,981
8,021	1,980
8,022	1,979
8,023	1,978
8,024	1,977

Hour	COUNTDOWN
8,025	1,976
8,026	1,975
8,027	1,974
8,028	1,973
8,029	1,972
8,030	1,971
8,031	1,970
8,032	1,969
8,033	1,968
8,034	1,967
8,035	1,966
8,036	1,965
8,037	1,964
8,038	1,963
8,039	1,962
8,040	1,961
8,041	1,960

Hour	COUNTDOWN
8,042	1,959
8,043	1,958
8,044	1,957
8,045	1,956
8,046	1,955
8,047	1,954
8,048	1,953
8,049	1,952
8,050	1,951
8,051	1,950
8,052	1,949
8,053	1,948
8,054	1,947
8,055	1,946
8,056	1,945
8,057	1,944
8,058	1,943

Hour	COUNTDOWN
8,059	1,942
8,060	1,941
8,061	1,940
8,062	1,939
8,063	1,938
8,064	1,937
8,065	1,936
8,066	1,935
8,067	1,934
8,068	1,933
8,069	1,932
8,070	1,931
8,071	1,930
8,072	1,929
8,073	1,928
8,074	1,927
8,075	1,926

Hour	COUNTDOWN
8,076	1,925
8,077	1,924
8,078	1,923
8,079	1,922
8,080	1,921
8,081	1,920
8,082	1,919
8,083	1,918
8,084	1,917
8,085	1,916
8,086	1,915
8,087	1,914
8,088	1,913
8,089	1,912
8,090	1,911
8,091	1,910
8,092	1,909

Hour	COUNTDOWN
8,093	1,908
8,094	1,907
8,095	1,906
8,096	1,905
8,097	1,904
8,098	1,903
8,099	1,902
8,100	1,901
8,101	1,900
8,102	1,899
8,103	1,898
8,104	1,897
8,105	1,896
8,106	1,895
8,107	1,894
8,108	1,893
8,109	1,892

Hour	COUNTDOWN
8,110	1,891
8,111	1,890
8,112	1,889
8,113	1,888
8,114	1,887
8,115	1,886
8,116	1,885
8,117	1,884
8,118	1,883
8,119	1,882
8,120	1,881
8,121	1,880
8,122	1,879
8,123	1,878
8,124	1,877
8,125	1,876
8,126	1,875

Hour	COUNTDOWN
8,127	1,874
8,128	1,873
8,129	1,872
8,130	1,871
8,131	1,870
8,132	1,869
8,133	1,868
8,134	1,867
8,135	1,866
8,136	1,865
8,137	1,864
8,138	1,863
8,139	1,862
8,140	1,861
8,141	1,860
8,142	1,859
8,143	1,858

Hour	COUNTDOWN
8,144	1,857
8,145	1,856
8,146	1,855
8,147	1,854
8,148	1,853
8,149	1,852
8,150	1,851
8,151	1,850
8,152	1,849
8,153	1,848
8,154	1,847
8,155	1,846
8,156	1,845
8,157	1,844
8,158	1,843
8,159	1,842
8,160	1,841

Hour	COUNTDOWN
8,161	1,840
8,162	1,839
8,163	1,838
8,164	1,837
8,165	1,836
8,166	1,835
8,167	1,834
8,168	1,833
8,169	1,832
8,170	1,831
8,171	1,830
8,172	1,829
8,173	1,828
8,174	1,827
8,175	1,826
8,176	1,825
8,177	1,824

Hour	COUNTDOWN
8,178	1,823
8,179	1,822
8,180	1,821
8,181	1,820
8,182	1,819
8,183	1,818
8,184	1,817
8,185	1,816
8,186	1,815
8,187	1,814
8,188	1,813
8,189	1,812
8,190	1,811
8,191	1,810
8,192	1,809
8,193	1,808
8,194	1,807

Hour	COUNTDOWN
8,195	1,806
8,196	1,805
8,197	1,804
8,198	1,803
8,199	1,802
8,200	1,801
8,201	1,800
8,202	1,799
8,203	1,798
8,204	1,797
8,205	1,796
8,206	1,795
8,207	1,794
8,208	1,793
8,209	1,792
8,210	1,791
8,211	1,790

Hour	COUNTDOWN
8,212	1,789
8,213	1,788
8,214	1,787
8,215	1,786
8,216	1,785
8,217	1,784
8,218	1,783
8,219	1,782
8,220	1,781
8,221	1,780
8,222	1,779
8,223	1,778
8,224	1,777
8,225	1,776
8,226	1,775
8,227	1,774
8,228	1,773

Hour	COUNTDOWN
8,229	1,772
8,230	1,771
8,231	1,770
8,232	1,769
8,233	1,768
8,234	1,767
8,235	1,766
8,236	1,765
8,237	1,764
8,238	1,763
8,239	1,762
8,240	1,761
8,241	1,760
8,242	1,759
8,243	1,758
8,244	1,757
8,245	1,756

Hour	COUNTDOWN
8,246	1,755
8,247	1,754
8,248	1,753
8,249	1,752
8,250	1,751
8,251	1,750
8,252	1,749
8,253	1,748
8,254	1,747
8,255	1,746
8,256	1,745
8,257	1,744
8,258	1,743
8,259	1,742
8,260	1,741
8,261	1,740
8,262	1,739

Hour	COUNTDOWN
8,263	1,738
8,264	1,737
8,265	1,736
8,266	1,735
8,267	1,734
8,268	1,733
8,269	1,732
8,270	1,731
8,271	1,730
8,272	1,729
8,273	1,728
8,274	1,727
8,275	1,726
8,276	1,725
8,277	1,724
8,278	1,723
8,279	1,722

Hour	COUNTDOWN
8,280	1,721
8,281	1,720
8,282	1,719
8,283	1,718
8,284	1,717
8,285	1,716
8,286	1,715
8,287	1,714
8,288	1,713
8,289	1,712
8,290	1,711
8,291	1,710
8,292	1,709
8,293	1,708
8,294	1,707
8,295	1,706
8,296	1,705

Hour	COUNTDOWN
8,297	1,704
8,298	1,703
8,299	1,702
8,300	1,701
8,301	1,700
8,302	1,699
8,303	1,698
8,304	1,697
8,305	1,696
8,306	1,695
8,307	1,694
8,308	1,693
8,309	1,692
8,310	1,691
8,311	1,690
8,312	1,689
8,313	1,688

Hour	COUNTDOWN
8,314	1,687
8,315	1,686
8,316	1,685
8,317	1,684
8,318	1,683
8,319	1,682
8,320	1,681
8,321	1,680
8,322	1,679
8,323	1,678
8,324	1,677
8,325	1,676
8,326	1,675
8,327	1,674
8,328	1,673
8,329	1,672
8,330	1,671

Hour	COUNTDOWN
8,331	1,670
8,332	1,669
8,333	1,668
8,334	1,667
8,335	1,666
8,336	1,665
8,337	1,664
8,338	1,663
8,339	1,662
8,340	1,661
8,341	1,660
8,342	1,659
8,343	1,658
8,344	1,657
8,345	1,656
8,346	1,655
8,347	1,654

Hour	COUNTDOWN
8,348	1,653
8,349	1,652
8,350	1,651
8,351	1,650
8,352	1,649
8,353	1,648
8,354	1,647
8,355	1,646
8,356	1,645
8,357	1,644
8,358	1,643
8,359	1,642
8,360	1,641
8,361	1,640
8,362	1,639
8,363	1,638
8,364	1,637

Hour	COUNTDOWN
8,365	1,636
8,366	1,635
8,367	1,634
8,368	1,633
8,369	1,632
8,370	1,631
8,371	1,630
8,372	1,629
8,373	1,628
8,374	1,627
8,375	1,626
8,376	1,625
8,377	1,624
8,378	1,623
8,379	1,622
8,380	1,621
8,381	1,620

Hour	COUNTDOWN
8,382	1,619
8,383	1,618
8,384	1,617
8,385	1,616
8,386	1,615
8,387	1,614
8,388	1,613
8,389	1,612
8,390	1,611
8,391	1,610
8,392	1,609
8,393	1,608
8,394	1,607
8,395	1,606
8,396	1,605
8,397	1,604
8,398	1,603

Hour	COUNTDOWN
8,399	1,602
8,400	1,601
8,401	1,600
8,402	1,599
8,403	1,598
8,404	1,597
8,405	1,596
8,406	1,595
8,407	1,594
8,408	1,593
8,409	1,592
8,410	1,591
8,411	1,590
8,412	1,589
8,413	1,588
8,414	1,587
8,415	1,586

Hour	COUNTDOWN
8,416	1,585
8,417	1,584
8,418	1,583
8,419	1,582
8,420	1,581
8,421	1,580
8,422	1,579
8,423	1,578
8,424	1,577
8,425	1,576
8,426	1,575
8,427	1,574
8,428	1,573
8,429	1,572
8,430	1,571
8,431	1,570
8,432	1,569

Hour	COUNTDOWN
8,433	1,568
8,434	1,567
8,435	1,566
8,436	1,565
8,437	1,564
8,438	1,563
8,439	1,562
8,440	1,561
8,441	1,560
8,442	1,559
8,443	1,558
8,444	1,557
8,445	1,556
8,446	1,555
8,447	1,554
8,448	1,553
8,449	1,552

Hour	COUNTDOWN
8,450	1,551
8,451	1,550
8,452	1,549
8,453	1,548
8,454	1,547
8,455	1,546
8,456	1,545
8,457	1,544
8,458	1,543
8,459	1,542
8,460	1,541
8,461	1,540
8,462	1,539
8,463	1,538
8,464	1,537
8,465	1,536
8,466	1,535

Hour	COUNTDOWN
8,467	1,534
8,468	1,533
8,469	1,532
8,470	1,531
8,471	1,530
8,472	1,529
8,473	1,528
8,474	1,527
8,475	1,526
8,476	1,525
8,477	1,524
8,478	1,523
8,479	1,522
8,480	1,521
8,481	1,520
8,482	1,519
8,483	1,518

Hour	COUNTDOWN
8,484	1,517
8,485	1,516
8,486	1,515
8,487	1,514
8,488	1,513
8,489	1,512
8,490	1,511
8,491	1,510
8,492	1,509
8,493	1,508
8,494	1,507
8,495	1,506
8,496	1,505
8,497	1,504
8,498	1,503
8,499	1,502
8,500	1,501

Hour	COUNTDOWN
8,501	1,500
8,502	1,499
8,503	1,498
8,504	1,497
8,505	1,496
8,506	1,495
8,507	1,494
8,508	1,493
8,509	1,492
8,510	1,491
8,511	1,490
8,512	1,489
8,513	1,488
8,514	1,487
8,515	1,486
8,516	1,485
8,517	1,484

Hour	COUNTDOWN
8,518	1,483
8,519	1,482
8,520	1,481
8,521	1,480
8,522	1,479
8,523	1,478
8,524	1,477
8,525	1,476
8,526	1,475
8,527	1,474
8,528	1,473
8,529	1,472
8,530	1,471
8,531	1,470
8,532	1,469
8,533	1,468
8,534	1,467

Hour	COUNTDOWN
8,535	1,466
8,536	1,465
8,537	1,464
8,538	1,463
8,539	1,462
8,540	1,461
8,541	1,460
8,542	1,459
8,543	1,458
8,544	1,457
8,545	1,456
8,546	1,455
8,547	1,454
8,548	1,453
8,549	1,452
8,550	1,451
8,551	1,450

Hour	COUNTDOWN
8,552	1,449
8,553	1,448
8,554	1,447
8,555	1,446
8,556	1,445
8,557	1,444
8,558	1,443
8,559	1,442
8,560	1,441
8,561	1,440
8,562	1,439
8,563	1,438
8,564	1,437
8,565	1,436
8,566	1,435
8,567	1,434
8,568	1,433

Hour	COUNTDOWN
8,569	1,432
8,570	1,431
8,571	1,430
8,572	1,429
8,573	1,428
8,574	1,427
8,575	1,426
8,576	1,425
8,577	1,424
8,578	1,423
8,579	1,422
8,580	1,421
8,581	1,420
8,582	1,419
8,583	1,418
8,584	1,417
8,585	1,416

Hour	COUNTDOWN
8,586	1,415
8,587	1,414
8,588	1,413
8,589	1,412
8,590	1,411
8,591	1,410
8,592	1,409
8,593	1,408
8,594	1,407
8,595	1,406
8,596	1,405
8,597	1,404
8,598	1,403
8,599	1,402
8,600	1,401
8,601	1,400
8,602	1,399

Hour	COUNTDOWN
8,603	1,398
8,604	1,397
8,605	1,396
8,606	1,395
8,607	1,394
8,608	1,393
8,609	1,392
8,610	1,391
8,611	1,390
8,612	1,389
8,613	1,388
8,614	1,387
8,615	1,386
8,616	1,385
8,617	1,384
8,618	1,383
8,619	1,382

Hour	COUNTDOWN
8,620	1,381
8,621	1,380
8,622	1,379
8,623	1,378
8,624	1,377
8,625	1,376
8,626	1,375
8,627	1,374
8,628	1,373
8,629	1,372
8,630	1,371
8,631	1,370
8,632	1,369
8,633	1,368
8,634	1,367
8,635	1,366
8,636	1,365

Hour	COUNTDOWN
8,637	1,364
8,638	1,363
8,639	1,362
8,640	1,361
8,641	1,360
8,642	1,359
8,643	1,358
8,644	1,357
8,645	1,356
8,646	1,355
8,647	1,354
8,648	1,353
8,649	1,352
8,650	1,351
8,651	1,350
8,652	1,349
8,653	1,348

Hour	COUNTDOWN
8,654	1,347
8,655	1,346
8,656	1,345
8,657	1,344
8,658	1,343
8,659	1,342
8,660	1,341
8,661	1,340
8,662	1,339
8,663	1,338
8,664	1,337
8,665	1,336
8,666	1,335
8,667	1,334
8,668	1,333
8,669	1,332
8,670	1,331

Hour	COUNTDOWN
8,671	1,330
8,672	1,329
8,673	1,328
8,674	1,327
8,675	1,326
8,676	1,325
8,677	1,324
8,678	1,323
8,679	1,322
8,680	1,321
8,681	1,320
8,682	1,319
8,683	1,318
8,684	1,317
8,685	1,316
8,686	1,315
8,687	1,314

Hour	COUNTDOWN
8,688	1,313
8,689	1,312
8,690	1,311
8,691	1,310
8,692	1,309
8,693	1,308
8,694	1,307
8,695	1,306
8,696	1,305
8,697	1,304
8,698	1,303
8,699	1,302
8,700	1,301
8,701	1,300
8,702	1,299
8,703	1,298
8,704	1,297

Hour	COUNTDOWN
8,705	1,296
8,706	1,295
8,707	1,294
8,708	1,293
8,709	1,292
8,710	1,291
8,711	1,290
8,712	1,289
8,713	1,288
8,714	1,287
8,715	1,286
8,716	1,285
8,717	1,284
8,718	1,283
8,719	1,282
8,720	1,281
8,721	1,280

Hour	COUNTDOWN
8,722	1,279
8,723	1,278
8,724	1,277
8,725	1,276
8,726	1,275
8,727	1,274
8,728	1,273
8,729	1,272
8,730	1,271
8,731	1,270
8,732	1,269
8,733	1,268
8,734	1,267
8,735	1,266
8,736	1,265
8,737	1,264
8,738	1,263

Hour	COUNTDOWN
8,739	1,262
8,740	1,261
8,741	1,260
8,742	1,259
8,743	1,258
8,744	1,257
8,745	1,256
8,746	1,255
8,747	1,254
8,748	1,253
8,749	1,252
8,750	1,251
8,751	1,250
8,752	1,249
8,753	1,248
8,754	1,247
8,755	1,246

Hour	COUNTDOWN
8,756	1,245
8,757	1,244
8,758	1,243
8,759	1,242
8,760	1,241
8,761	1,240
8,762	1,239
8,763	1,238
8,764	1,237
8,765	1,236
8,766	1,235
8,767	1,234
8,768	1,233
8,769	1,232
8,770	1,231
8,771	1,230
8,772	1,229

Hour	COUNTDOWN
8,773	1,228
8,774	1,227
8,775	1,226
8,776	1,225
8,777	1,224
8,778	1,223
8,779	1,222
8,780	1,221
8,781	1,220
8,782	1,219
8,783	1,218
8,784	1,217
8,785	1,216
8,786	1,215
8,787	1,214
8,788	1,213
8,789	1,212

Hour	COUNTDOWN
8,790	1,211
8,791	1,210
8,792	1,209
8,793	1,208
8,794	1,207
8,795	1,206
8,796	1,205
8,797	1,204
8,798	1,203
8,799	1,202
8,800	1,201
8,801	1,200
8,802	1,199
8,803	1,198
8,804	1,197
8,805	1,196
8,806	1,195

Hour	COUNTDOWN
8,807	1,194
8,808	1,193
8,809	1,192
8,810	1,191
8,811	1,190
8,812	1,189
8,813	1,188
8,814	1,187
8,815	1,186
8,816	1,185
8,817	1,184
8,818	1,183
8,819	1,182
8,820	1,181
8,821	1,180
8,822	1,179
8,823	1,178

Hour	COUNTDOWN
8,824	1,177
8,825	1,176
8,826	1,175
8,827	1,174
8,828	1,173
8,829	1,172
8,830	1,171
8,831	1,170
8,832	1,169
8,833	1,168
8,834	1,167
8,835	1,166
8,836	1,165
8,837	1,164
8,838	1,163
8,839	1,162
8,840	1,161

Hour	COUNTDOWN
8,841	1,160
8,842	1,159
8,843	1,158
8,844	1,157
8,845	1,156
8,846	1,155
8,847	1,154
8,848	1,153
8,849	1,152
8,850	1,151
8,851	1,150
8,852	1,149
8,853	1,148
8,854	1,147
8,855	1,146
8,856	1,145
8,857	1,144

Hour	COUNTDOWN
8,858	1,143
8,859	1,142
8,860	1,141
8,861	1,140
8,862	1,139
8,863	1,138
8,864	1,137
8,865	1,136
8,866	1,135
8,867	1,134
8,868	1,133
8,869	1,132
8,870	1,131
8,871	1,130
8,872	1,129
8,873	1,128
8,874	1,127

Hour	COUNTDOWN
8,875	1,126
8,876	1,125
8,877	1,124
8,878	1,123
8,879	1,122
8,880	1,121
8,881	1,120
8,882	1,119
8,883	1,118
8,884	1,117
8,885	1,116
8,886	1,115
8,887	1,114
8,888	1,113
8,889	1,112
8,890	1,111
8,891	1,110

Hour	COUNTDOWN
8,892	1,109
8,893	1,108
8,894	1,107
8,895	1,106
8,896	1,105
8,897	1,104
8,898	1,103
8,899	1,102
8,900	1,101
8,901	1,100
8,902	1,099
8,903	1,098
8,904	1,097
8,905	1,096
8,906	1,095
8,907	1,094
8,908	1,093

Hour	COUNTDOWN
8,909	1,092
8,910	1,091
8,911	1,090
8,912	1,089
8,913	1,088
8,914	1,087
8,915	1,086
8,916	1,085
8,917	1,084
8,918	1,083
8,919	1,082
8,920	1,081
8,921	1,080
8,922	1,079
8,923	1,078
8,924	1,077
8,925	1,076

Hour	COUNTDOWN
8,926	1,075
8,927	1,074
8,928	1,073
8,929	1,072
8,930	1,071
8,931	1,070
8,932	1,069
8,933	1,068
8,934	1,067
8,935	1,066
8,936	1,065
8,937	1,064
8,938	1,063
8,939	1,062
8,940	1,061
8,941	1,060
8,942	1,059

Hour	COUNTDOWN
8,943	1,058
8,944	1,057
8,945	1,056
8,946	1,055
8,947	1,054
8,948	1,053
8,949	1,052
8,950	1,051
8,951	1,050
8,952	1,049
8,953	1,048
8,954	1,047
8,955	1,046
8,956	1,045
8,957	1,044
8,958	1,043
8,959	1,042

Hour	COUNTDOWN
8,960	1,041
8,961	1,040
8,962	1,039
8,963	1,038
8,964	1,037
8,965	1,036
8,966	1,035
8,967	1,034
8,968	1,033
8,969	1,032
8,970	1,031
8,971	1,030
8,972	1,029
8,973	1,028
8,974	1,027
8,975	1,026
8,976	1,025

Hour	COUNTDOWN
8,977	1,024
8,978	1,023
8,979	1,022
8,980	1,021
8,981	1,020
8,982	1,019
8,983	1,018
8,984	1,017
8,985	1,016
8,986	1,015
8,987	1,014
8,988	1,013
8,989	1,012
8,990	1,011
8,991	1,010
8,992	1,009
8,993	1,008

Hour	COUNTDOWN
8,994	1,007
8,995	1,006
8,996	1,005
8,997	1,004
8,998	1,003
8,999	1,002
9,000	1,001
9,001	1,000
9,002	999
9,003	998
9,004	997
9,005	996
9,006	995
9,007	994
9,008	993
9,009	992
9,010	991

Hour	COUNTDOWN
9,011	990
9,012	989
9,013	988
9,014	987
9,015	986
9,016	985
9,017	984
9,018	983
9,019	982
9,020	981
9,021	980
9,022	979
9,023	978
9,024	977
9,025	976
9,026	975
9,027	974

Hour	COUNTDOWN
9,028	973
9,029	972
9,030	971
9,031	970
9,032	969
9,033	968
9,034	967
9,035	966
9,036	965
9,037	964
9,038	963
9,039	962
9,040	961
9,041	960
9,042	959
9,043	958
9,044	957

Hour	COUNTDOWN
9,045	956
9,046	955
9,047	954
9,048	953
9,049	952
9,050	951
9,051	950
9,052	949
9,053	948
9,054	947
9,055	946
9,056	945
9,057	944
9,058	943
9,059	942
9,060	941
9,061	940

Hour	COUNTDOWN
9,062	939
9,063	938
9,064	937
9,065	936
9,066	935
9,067	934
9,068	933
9,069	932
9,070	931
9,071	930
9,072	929
9,073	928
9,074	927
9,075	926
9,076	925
9,077	924
9,078	923

Hour	COUNTDOWN
9,079	922
9,080	921
9,081	920
9,082	919
9,083	918
9,084	917
9,085	916
9,086	915
9,087	914
9,088	913
9,089	912
9,090	911
9,091	910
9,092	909
9,093	908
9,094	907
9,095	906

Hour	COUNTDOWN
9,096	905
9,097	904
9,098	903
9,099	902
9,100	901
9,101	900
9,102	899
9,103	898
9,104	897
9,105	896
9,106	895
9,107	894
9,108	893
9,109	892
9,110	891
9,111	890
9,112	889

Hour	COUNTDOWN
9,113	888
9,114	887
9,115	886
9,116	885
9,117	884
9,118	883
9,119	882
9,120	881
9,121	880
9,122	879
9,123	878
9,124	877
9,125	876
9,126	875
9,127	874
9,128	873
9,129	872

Hour	COUNTDOWN
9,130	871
9,131	870
9,132	869
9,133	868
9,134	867
9,135	866
9,136	865
9,137	864
9,138	863
9,139	862
9,140	861
9,141	860
9,142	859
9,143	858
9,144	857
9,145	856
9,146	855

Hour	COUNTDOWN
9,147	854
9,148	853
9,149	852
9,150	851
9,151	850
9,152	849
9,153	848
9,154	847
9,155	846
9,156	845
9,157	844
9,158	843
9,159	842
9,160	841
9,161	840
9,162	839
9,163	838

Hour	COUNTDOWN
9,164	837
9,165	836
9,166	835
9,167	834
9,168	833
9,169	832
9,170	831
9,171	830
9,172	829
9,173	828
9,174	827
9,175	826
9,176	825
9,177	824
9,178	823
9,179	822
9,180	821

Hour	COUNTDOWN
9,181	820
9,182	819
9,183	818
9,184	817
9,185	816
9,186	815
9,187	814
9,188	813
9,189	812
9,190	811
9,191	810
9,192	809
9,193	808
9,194	807
9,195	806
9,196	805
9,197	804

Hour	COUNTDOWN
9,198	803
9,199	802
9,200	801
9,201	800
9,202	799
9,203	798
9,204	797
9,205	796
9,206	795
9,207	794
9,208	793
9,209	792
9,210	791
9,211	790
9,212	789
9,213	788
9,214	787

Hour	COUNTDOWN
9,215	786
9,216	785
9,217	784
9,218	783
9,219	782
9,220	781
9,221	780
9,222	779
9,223	778
9,224	777
9,225	776
9,226	775
9,227	774
9,228	773
9,229	772
9,230	771
9,231	770

Hour	COUNTDOWN
9,232	769
9,233	768
9,234	767
9,235	766
9,236	765
9,237	764
9,238	763
9,239	762
9,240	761
9,241	760
9,242	759
9,243	758
9,244	757
9,245	756
9,246	755
9,247	754
9,248	753

Hour	COUNTDOWN
9,249	752
9,250	751
9,251	750
9,252	749
9,253	748
9,254	747
9,255	746
9,256	745
9,257	744
9,258	743
9,259	742
9,260	741
9,261	740
9,262	739
9,263	738
9,264	737
9,265	736

Hour	COUNTDOWN
9,266	735
9,267	734
9,268	733
9,269	732
9,270	731
9,271	730
9,272	729
9,273	728
9,274	727
9,275	726
9,276	725
9,277	724
9,278	723
9,279	722
9,280	721
9,281	720
9,282	719

Hour	COUNTDOWN
9,283	718
9,284	717
9,285	716
9,286	715
9,287	714
9,288	713
9,289	712
9,290	711
9,291	710
9,292	709
9,293	708
9,294	707
9,295	706
9,296	705
9,297	704
9,298	703
9,299	702

Hour	COUNTDOWN
9,300	701
9,301	700
9,302	699
9,303	698
9,304	697
9,305	696
9,306	695
9,307	694
9,308	693
9,309	692
9,310	691
9,311	690
9,312	689
9,313	688
9,314	687
9,315	686
9,316	685

Hour	COUNTDOWN
9,317	684
9,318	683
9,319	682
9,320	681
9,321	680
9,322	679
9,323	678
9,324	677
9,325	676
9,326	675
9,327	674
9,328	673
9,329	672
9,330	671
9,331	670
9,332	669
9,333	668

Hour	COUNTDOWN
9,334	667
9,335	666
9,336	665
9,337	664
9,338	663
9,339	662
9,340	661
9,341	660
9,342	659
9,343	658
9,344	657
9,345	656
9,346	655
9,347	654
9,348	653
9,349	652
9,350	651

Hour	COUNTDOWN
9,351	650
9,352	649
9,353	648
9,354	647
9,355	646
9,356	645
9,357	644
9,358	643
9,359	642
9,360	641
9,361	640
9,362	639
9,363	638
9,364	637
9,365	636
9,366	635
9,367	634

Hour	COUNTDOWN
9,368	633
9,369	632
9,370	631
9,371	630
9,372	629
9,373	628
9,374	627
9,375	626
9,376	625
9,377	624
9,378	623
9,379	622
9,380	621
9,381	620
9,382	619
9,383	618
9,384	617

Hour	COUNTDOWN
9,385	616
9,386	615
9,387	614
9,388	613
9,389	612
9,390	611
9,391	610
9,392	609
9,393	608
9,394	607
9,395	606
9,396	605
9,397	604
9,398	603
9,399	602
9,400	601
9,401	600

Hour	COUNTDOWN
9,402	599
9,403	598
9,404	597
9,405	596
9,406	595
9,407	594
9,408	593
9,409	592
9,410	591
9,411	590
9,412	589
9,413	588
9,414	587
9,415	586
9,416	585
9,417	584
9,418	583

Hour	COUNTDOWN
9,419	582
9,420	581
9,421	580
9,422	579
9,423	578
9,424	577
9,425	576
9,426	575
9,427	574
9,428	573
9,429	572
9,430	571
9,431	570
9,432	569
9,433	568
9,434	567
9,435	566

Hour	COUNTDOWN
9,436	565
9,437	564
9,438	563
9,439	562
9,440	561
9,441	560
9,442	559
9,443	558
9,444	557
9,445	556
9,446	555
9,447	554
9,448	553
9,449	552
9,450	551
9,451	550
9,452	549

Hour	COUNTDOWN
9,453	548
9,454	547
9,455	546
9,456	545
9,457	544
9,458	543
9,459	542
9,460	541
9,461	540
9,462	539
9,463	538
9,464	537
9,465	536
9,466	535
9,467	534
9,468	533
9,469	532

Hour	COUNTDOWN
9,470	531
9,471	530
9,472	529
9,473	528
9,474	527
9,475	526
9,476	525
9,477	524
9,478	523
9,479	522
9,480	521
9,481	520
9,482	519
9,483	518
9,484	517
9,485	516
9,486	515

Hour	COUNTDOWN
9,487	514
9,488	513
9,489	512
9,490	511
9,491	510
9,492	509
9,493	508
9,494	507
9,495	506
9,496	505
9,497	504
9,498	503
9,499	502
9,500	501
9,501	500
9,502	499
9,503	498

Hour	COUNTDOWN
9,504	497
9,505	496
9,506	495
9,507	494
9,508	493
9,509	492
9,510	491
9,511	490
9,512	489
9,513	488
9,514	487
9,515	486
9,516	485
9,517	484
9,518	483
9,519	482
9,520	481

Hour	COUNTDOWN
9,521	480
9,522	479
9,523	478
9,524	477
9,525	476
9,526	475
9,527	474
9,528	473
9,529	472
9,530	471
9,531	470
9,532	469
9,533	468
9,534	467
9,535	466
9,536	465
9,537	464

Hour	COUNTDOWN
9,538	463
9,539	462
9,540	461
9,541	460
9,542	459
9,543	458
9,544	457
9,545	456
9,546	455
9,547	454
9,548	453
9,549	452
9,550	451
9,551	450
9,552	449
9,553	448
9,554	447

Hour	COUNTDOWN
9,555	446
9,556	445
9,557	444
9,558	443
9,559	442
9,560	441
9,561	440
9,562	439
9,563	438
9,564	437
9,565	436
9,566	435
9,567	434
9,568	433
9,569	432
9,570	431
9,571	430

Hour	COUNTDOWN
9,572	429
9,573	428
9,574	427
9,575	426
9,576	425
9,577	424
9,578	423
9,579	422
9,580	421
9,581	420
9,582	419
9,583	418
9,584	417
9,585	416
9,586	415
9,587	414
9,588	413

Hour	COUNTDOWN
9,589	412
9,590	411
9,591	410
9,592	409
9,593	408
9,594	407
9,595	406
9,596	405
9,597	404
9,598	403
9,599	402
9,600	401
9,601	400
9,602	399
9,603	398
9,604	397
9,605	396

Hour	COUNTDOWN
9,606	395
9,607	394
9,608	393
9,609	392
9,610	391
9,611	390
9,612	389
9,613	388
9,614	387
9,615	386
9,616	385
9,617	384
9,618	383
9,619	382
9,620	381
9,621	380
9,622	379

Hour	COUNTDOWN
9,623	378
9,624	377
9,625	376
9,626	375
9,627	374
9,628	373
9,629	372
9,630	371
9,631	370
9,632	369
9,633	368
9,634	367
9,635	366
9,636	365
9,637	364
9,638	363
9,639	362

Hour	COUNTDOWN
9,640	361
9,641	360
9,642	359
9,643	358
9,644	357
9,645	356
9,646	355
9,647	354
9,648	353
9,649	352
9,650	351
9,651	350
9,652	349
9,653	348
9,654	347
9,655	346
9,656	345

Hour	COUNTDOWN
9,657	344
9,658	343
9,659	342
9,660	341
9,661	340
9,662	339
9,663	338
9,664	337
9,665	336
9,666	335
9,667	334
9,668	333
9,669	332
9,670	331
9,671	330
9,672	329
9,673	328

Hour	COUNTDOWN
9,674	327
9,675	326
9,676	325
9,677	324
9,678	323
9,679	322
9,680	321
9,681	320
9,682	319
9,683	318
9,684	317
9,685	316
9,686	315
9,687	314
9,688	313
9,689	312
9,690	311

Hour	COUNTDOWN
9,691	310
9,692	309
9,693	308
9,694	307
9,695	306
9,696	305
9,697	304
9,698	303
9,699	302
9,700	301
9,701	300
9,702	299
9,703	298
9,704	297
9,705	296
9,706	295
9,707	294

Hour	COUNTDOWN
9,708	293
9,709	292
9,710	291
9,711	290
9,712	289
9,713	288
9,714	287
9,715	286
9,716	285
9,717	284
9,718	283
9,719	282
9,720	281
9,721	280
9,722	279
9,723	278
9,724	277

Hour	COUNTDOWN
9,725	276
9,726	275
9,727	274
9,728	273
9,729	272
9,730	271
9,731	270
9,732	269
9,733	268
9,734	267
9,735	266
9,736	265
9,737	264
9,738	263
9,739	262
9,740	261
9,741	260

Hour	COUNTDOWN
9,742	259
9,743	258
9,744	257
9,745	256
9,746	255
9,747	254
9,748	253
9,749	252
9,750	251
9,751	250
9,752	249
9,753	248
9,754	247
9,755	246
9,756	245
9,757	244
9,758	243

Hour	COUNTDOWN
9,759	242
9,760	241
9,761	240
9,762	239
9,763	238
9,764	237
9,765	236
9,766	235
9,767	234
9,768	233
9,769	232
9,770	231
9,771	230
9,772	229
9,773	228
9,774	227
9,775	226

Hour	COUNTDOWN
9,776	225
9,777	224
9,778	223
9,779	222
9,780	221
9,781	220
9,782	219
9,783	218
9,784	217
9,785	216
9,786	215
9,787	214
9,788	213
9,789	212
9,790	211
9,791	210
9,792	209

Hour	COUNTDOWN
9,793	208
9,794	207
9,795	206
9,796	205
9,797	204
9,798	203
9,799	202
9,800	201
9,801	200
9,802	199
9,803	198
9,804	197
9,805	196
9,806	195
9,807	194
9,808	193
9,809	192

Hour	COUNTDOWN
9,810	191
9,811	190
9,812	189
9,813	188
9,814	187
9,815	186
9,816	185
9,817	184
9,818	183
9,819	182
9,820	181
9,821	180
9,822	179
9,823	178
9,824	177
9,825	176
9,826	175

Hour	COUNTDOWN
9,827	174
9,828	173
9,829	172
9,830	171
9,831	170
9,832	169
9,833	168
9,834	167
9,835	166
9,836	165
9,837	164
9,838	163
9,839	162
9,840	161
9,841	160
9,842	159
9,843	158

Hour	COUNTDOWN
9,844	157
9,845	156
9,846	155
9,847	154
9,848	153
9,849	152
9,850	151
9,851	150
9,852	149
9,853	148
9,854	147
9,855	146
9,856	145
9,857	144
9,858	143
9,859	142
9,860	141

Hour	COUNTDOWN
9,861	140
9,862	139
9,863	138
9,864	137
9,865	136
9,866	135
9,867	134
9,868	133
9,869	132
9,870	131
9,871	130
9,872	129
9,873	128
9,874	127
9,875	126
9,876	125
9,877	124

Hour	COUNTDOWN
9,878	123
9,879	122
9,880	121
9,881	120
9,882	119
9,883	118
9,884	117
9,885	116
9,886	115
9,887	114
9,888	113
9,889	112
9,890	111
9,891	110
9,892	109
9,893	108
9,894	107

Hour	COUNTDOWN
9,895	106
9,896	105
9,897	104
9,898	103
9,899	102
9,900	101
9,901	100
9,902	99
9,903	98
9,904	97
9,905	96
9,906	95
9,907	94
9,908	93
9,909	92
9,910	91
9,911	90

Hour	COUNTDOWN
9,912	89
9,913	88
9,914	87
9,915	86
9,916	85
9,917	84
9,918	83
9,919	82
9,920	81
9,921	80
9,922	79
9,923	78
9,924	77
9,925	76
9,926	75
9,927	74
9,928	73

Hour	COUNTDOWN
9,929	72
9,930	71
9,931	70
9,932	69
9,933	68
9,934	67
9,935	66
9,936	65
9,937	64
9,938	63
9,939	62
9,940	61
9,941	60
9,942	59
9,943	58
9,944	57
9,945	56

Hour	COUNTDOWN
9,946	55
9,947	54
9,948	53
9,949	52
9,950	51
9,951	50
9,952	49
9,953	48
9,954	47
9,955	46
9,956	45
9,957	44
9,958	43
9,959	42
9,960	41
9,961	40
9,962	39

Hour	COUNTDOWN
9,963	38
9,964	37
9,965	36
9,966	35
9,967	34
9,968	33
9,969	32
9,970	31
9,971	30
9,972	29
9,973	28
9,974	27
9,975	26
9,976	25
9,977	24
9,978	23
9,979	22

Hour	COUNTDOWN
9,980	21
9,981	20
9,982	19
9,983	18
9,984	17
9,985	16
9,986	15
9,987	14
9,988	13
9,989	12
9,990	11
9,991	10
9,992	9
9,993	8
9,994	7
9,995	6
9,996	5

TAG INDEX

THIS TAG...	... IS FOUND ON THESE HOURS/PAGES

TAG INDEX

THIS TAG...	... IS FOUND ON THESE HOURS/PAGES

TAG INDEX

THIS TAG…	… IS FOUND ON THESE HOURS/PAGES

12771943R00342

Made in the USA
Lexington, KY
29 December 2011